THE ULTIMATE
VANCOUVER CANUCKS
TRIVIA BOOK

A Collection of Amazing Trivia Quizzes
and Fun Facts for Die-Hard Canucks Fans!

Ray Walker

Exclusive Free Book

Crazy Sports Stories

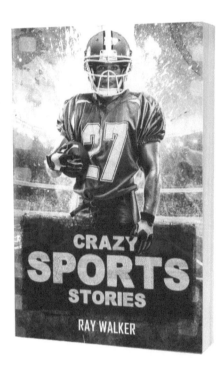

As a thank you for getting a copy of this book I would like to offer you a free copy of my book Crazy Sports Stories which comes packed with interesting stories from your favorite sports such as Football, Hockey, Baseball, Basketball and more.

Grab your free copy over at

RayWalkerMedia.com/Bonus

CONTENTS

Introduction

Team fandom is inspirational. Our attachment to our favorite teams fills us with pride, excitement, loyalty, and a sense of fulfillment in knowing that we are part of a community with many other fans who feel the same way.

Vancouver Canucks fans are no exception. With a rich, successful history in the NHL, the Canucks have inspired their supporters to strive for greatness with their tradition of colorful players, memorable eras, big moves, and unique moments.

This book is a celebration of those moments, and an examination of the collection of interesting, impressive, or important details that allow us to understand the full stories behind the players and the team.

You may use the book as you wish. Each chapter contains 20 quiz questions in a mixture of multiple-choice and true-false formats, an answer key (Don't worry, it's on a separate page!), and a section of ten "Did You Know?" factoids about the team.

Some will use it to test themselves with the quiz questions. How much Canucks history did you really know? How many of the finer points can you remember? Some will use it competitively (Isn't that the heart of sports?), waging contests with friends and fellow devotees to see who can lay claim to being the biggest fan. Some will enjoy it as a learning experience, gaining insight to enrich their fandom and add color to understanding their favorite team. Still, others may use it to teach, sharing the wonderful anecdotes inside to inspire a new generation of fans to hop aboard the Canucks bandwagon.

Whatever your purpose may be, we hope you enjoy delving into Vancouver Canucks hockey's amazing background!

Oh…and for the record, information and statistics in this book are current to the beginning of 2020. The Canucks will surely topple more records and win more awards as the seasons pass, so keep this in mind when you're watching the next game with your friends, and someone starts a conversation with "Did you know…?".

CHAPTER 1:

ORIGINS & HISTORY

QUIZ TIME!

1. In which year did the Canucks begin playing in the National Hockey League?

    a. 1967
    b. 1970
    c. 1976
    d. 1980

2. Six players from Vancouver's WHL team were called up for the inaugural season of the Canucks.

    a. True
    b. False

3. How was the nickname "Canucks" chosen for the team?

    a. It was elected as the winner in a fan-balloting contest in the local newspaper.
    b. It was chosen by the owner's wife in an effort to appeal to the nation instead of just the region.

c. It was decided upon by the National Hockey league, with President Clarence Campbell having the final say.

d. It was adopted from Vancouver's minor league hockey team.

4. In which season did the Canucks begin to play in their new home, Rogers Arena (formerly General Motors Place)?

   a. 1985
   b. 1990
   c. 1995
   d. 2000

5. Who was the founder of the Vancouver Canucks?

   a. Entrepreneur Tom Scallen, from Minnesota
   b. Media magnate Conrad Black, from Ottawa
   c. Fishing mogul Michael Wilson, from Vancouver
   d. Real estate tycoon George Steinbrenner, from New York

6. In which year did the Canucks earn their first-ever playoff series win?

   a. 1975
   b. 1982
   c. 1987
   d. 1991

7. The Vancouver Canucks have a winning record against every other Canadian NHL team.

   a. True
   b. False

8. How many times in their franchise history have the Canucks won a division title?

   a. 2
   b. 5
   c. 10
   d. 13

9. Who was the first Canuck ever to be named as Vancouver's representative in the NHL All-Star Game?

   a. Right winger Bobby Schmautz
   b. Defenseman Dale Tallon
   c. Center Thomas Gradin
   d. Left winger Tiger Williams

10. Where do the Vancouver Canucks rank among NHL franchises when it comes to most Stanley Cup championships won?

    a. 10th overall
    b. 15th overall
    c. 22nd overall
    d. Tied for last overall

11. How did the Canucks fare during their 40th anniversary season in the NHL?

    a. Missed the playoffs
    b. Lost in 5 games in the first round to the Chicago Blackhawks
    c. Lost in 6 games in the third round to the San Jose Sharks

d. Lost in 7 games in the Stanley Cup Finals to the Boston Bruins

12. When the Canucks joined the NHL, they were slotted into the East Division, despite being located on the west coast of Canada.

   a. True
   b. False

13. Which team did Vancouver face in its first-ever NHL game (which resulted in a 3-1 loss for the Canucks)?

   a. California Golden Seals
   b. Buffalo Sabres
   c. Los Angeles Kings
   d. New York Rangers

14. Vancouver's current top farm team plays in the American Hockey League. What is this team called?

   a. San Antonio Rampage
   b. Hartford Wolf Pack
   c. Grand Rapids Griffins
   d. Utica Comets

15. Which player scored the first-ever goal for the Canucks?

   a. Defenseman Barry Wilkins
   b. Center Orland Kurtenbach
   c. Right winger Murray Hall
   d. Left winger Ted Taylor

16. Vancouver has sent more players to the Winter Olympics to represent their countries than any other NHL franchise.

a. True

b. False

17. How did Vancouver fare in its first-ever NHL playoff run?

a. Lost to the New York Islanders in the preliminary round

b. Lost to the Montreal Canadiens in the quarterfinals

c. Lost to the Chicago Blackhawks in the conference finals

d. Lost to the Detroit Red Wings in the Stanley Cup Finals

18. Which team did Vancouver defeat, 5-3, to earn their first win in franchise history on October 11, 1970?

a. Toronto Maple Leafs

b. New Jersey Devils

c. New York Islanders

d. Philadelphia Flyers

19. Vancouver used focus groups to select a mascot before the 2001-02 season. What was chosen as the name of the Canucks' mascot?

a. Luke the Logger

b. Monty the Mountie

c. Fin the Whale

d. Charlie the Chief

20. The Canucks are tied with the Buffalo Sabres as the oldest NHL franchises not to have won a Stanley Cup.

a. True

b. False

QUIZ ANSWERS

1. B – 1970

2. A – True

3. D – It was adopted from Vancouver's minor league hockey team.

4. C – 1995

5. A – Entrepreneur Tom Scallen, from Minnesota

6. B – 1982

7. B – False

8. C – 10

9. B – Defenseman Dale Tallon

10. D – Tied for last overall

11. D – Lost in 7 games in the Stanley Cup Finals to the Boston Bruins

12. A – True

13. C – Los Angeles Kings

14. D – Utica Comets

15. A – Defenseman Barry Wilkins

16. B – False

17. B – Lost to the Montreal Canadiens in the quarterfinals

18. A – Toronto Maple Leafs

19. C – Fin the Whale

20. A – True

DID YOU KNOW?

1. The NHL has shifted the Vancouver Canucks, along with many other teams, amongst many divisions as the league went through multiple restructurings. The Canucks began in the East Division, then moved into the Smythe Division of the Campbell Conference, were placed into the Pacific Division of the West Conference, slotted into the Northwest Division, then moved back to the Pacific Division of the West Conference, where they remain today.

2. Before the Canucks existed, there was a professional ice hockey team in Vancouver known as the Millionaires. They were founded in 1911 by Frank and Lester Patrick, and won the Stanley Cup in 1915, marking the first time it had ever been won by a team based in the West Coast.

3. Vancouver was initially denied an NHL expansion franchise in 1967. It was reported that this was partially because the Toronto Maple Leafs and Montreal Canadiens did not want to split television revenues from the Canadian Broadcasting Corporation with a third Canadian team.

4. The Canucks have shared their arena with fellow tenants from the National Lacrosse League (Ravens and Warriors), Roller Hockey International (Voodoo), and the National Basketball Association (Grizzlies). In 2020, they began

sharing the arena with the Vancouver Titans, a video game team that competes in the Overwatch League.

5. When the Canucks joined the National Hockey League, their expansion fee was $6 million. In today's dollars, that would equate to approximately $40 million.

6. The Canucks were nearly created through relocation rather than expansion. The Oakland Seals were struggling to draw fans and had a deal arranged to move to Vancouver, but the NHL did not want a franchise relocating so soon after its creation and vetoed the deal.

7. Vancouver does not have one specific main NHL rival team. Their main rivalries are considered to be with the Calgary Flames and Edmonton Oilers, due to geographic proximity and divisional competition. However, some fans consider the Boston Bruins or Chicago Blackhawks to be bigger rivals due to heated playoff series that have taken place between the teams in the past.

8. The Canucks posted only two winning seasons in their first twenty years of existence, but nevertheless made the playoffs eleven times during that span.

9. In the beginning, the Canucks struggled in the well-established East Division, finishing no higher than 6th and failing to make the playoffs in their first four seasons. When they were relocated to the Smythe Division before their fifth season, the team responded by finishing 1st and qualifying for their first playoffs.

10. The Canucks' successful 1974-75 season (noted above) was a key factor in the team remaining viable. The rival World Hockey Association had established the Vancouver Blazers, but the Canucks' popularity won them the market, and the Blazers moved to Alberta the next year.

CHAPTER 2:

JERSEYS & NUMBERS

QUIZ TIME!

1. When they began playing in the NHL, the Canucks used what color scheme for their uniforms?

   a. Black, orange, and gold

   b. Emerald green, red, and black

   c. Royal blue, Kelly green, and white

   d. Navy blue, sky blue, maroon, and silver

2. The numbers 0 and 00 have been banned from circulation by Vancouver's ownership, as they are seen to represent a losing attitude.

   a. True

   b. False

3. The Canucks hired a San Francisco design firm to update their look in 1978, and the company came up with new team colors and a V for a logo. What did the agency claim the V stood for?

a. Vancouver

b. Victory

c. Valiant

d. Valorous

4. The first time Vancouver worked the term "Canucks" into its logo was in 1985. Which of the following was NOT a term that this logo was known as?

a. The flying skate

b. The plate of spaghetti

c. The waffle iron

d. The blurred boot

5. Aside from the usual "Orca C" logo, what else have the Canucks frequently sported on the front of their jerseys in recent seasons?

a. A block lettered "B.C." to show support for their province

b. A maple leaf, staking claim to being Canada's team during the playoffs

c. Their original "stick in rink" logo to pay homage to their history

d. An outline in the shape of British Columbia with their logo in the location of Vancouver

6. Which jersey number has proven to be most popular with the Canucks, having been worn by 31 players?

a. 7

b. 9

c. 17

d. 21

7. Defenseman Ben Hutton wanted to wear number 10 in Vancouver, but it had been retired so he chose number 27 because he'd worn it one year in junior and won a championship that season.

   a. True

   b. False

8. Who is the player to wear the highest numbered jersey in Canucks franchise history?

   a. Alexander Mogilny

   b. Jared McCann

   c. Jay Beagle

   d. Pavel Bure

9. Why did veteran winger Derek Dorsett choose to wear number 51 on his jersey when traded to Vancouver?

   a. To honor his father, who had passed away the summer before at age 51.

   b. It was the inverse of number 15, which he had worn for over 300 NHL games already.

   c. He was 51 goals shy of 300 for his career, and wanted to reach that landmark.

   d. It represented his children, Max (age 5) and Dave (age 1).

10. Gino Odjick is the only Canuck to ever wear which uniform number?

a. 0

b. 40

c. 66

d. 99

11. Why did Vancouver add player names to the back of their jerseys at the beginning of the 1977-78 season?

   a. They had many new players on the team and wanted to make it easier for fans to identify them.

   b. The players requested it, feeling that they could make more money if they were more well-known as individuals.

   c. It was part of a sponsorship with a local sporting goods company.

   d. The NHL instituted a new rule making the names obligatory.

12. Star rookie Quinn Hughes is the only Canuck to have ever worn the number 43 on his jersey.

   a. True

   b. False

13. Who was the first player to have his number retired by the Vancouver Canucks?

   a. Trevor Linden

   b. Kirk McLean

   c. Roberto Luongo

   d. Stan Smyl

14. How many jersey numbers have the Vancouver Canucks retired for their former players?

    a. 3
    b. 6
    c. 9
    d. 12

15. Which player competed for the Canucks for just 7 seasons; the shortest tenure of anyone whose number has been retired by the franchise?

    a. Pavel Bure
    b. Stan Smyl
    c. Ed Jovanovski
    d. Markus Naslund

16. Sixteen players have worn number 1 for Vancouver, and every single one of them was a goaltender.

    a. True
    b. False

17. Lucky number 7 has been worn by sixteen Canucks players over the years. Which skater wore it for the longest amount of time?

    a. Linden Vey
    b. Cliff Ronning
    c. Brendan Morrison
    d. Gary Lupul

18. Who are the most recent Canucks players to have their numbers retired by the club?

a. Trevor Linden and Mark Messier

b. Markus Naslund and Todd Bertuzzi

c. Pavel Bure and Stan Smyl

d. Daniel Sedin and Henrik Sedin

19. Which number did Orland Kurtenbach, who was named the first captain in Canucks history, wear on the back of his jersey?

a. 70

b. 25

c. 9

d. 7

20. Pavel Bure's number 10 was the first number any NHL franchise retired in honor of a Russian player.

a. True

b. False

QUIZ ANSWERS

1. C – Royal blue, Kelly green, and white

2. B – False

3. B – Victory

4. D – The blurred boot

5. C – Their original "stick in rink" logo to pay homage to their history

6. C – 17

7. A – True

8. D – Pavel Bure, He wore number 96 for one season.

9. B – It was the inverse of number 15, which he had worn for over 300 NHL games already.

10. C – 66

11. D – The NHL instituted a new rule making the names obligatory.

12. A – True

13. D – Stan Smyl

14. B – 6

15. A – Pavel Bure

16. A – True

17. C – Brendan Morrison

18. D – Daniel Sedin and Henrik Sedin

19. B – 25

20. A – True

DID YOU KNOW?

1. Vancouver's original logo depicted a hockey stick within an ice rink. Very subtly, the position of the stick divided the ice into a C shape to stand for "Canucks." This was designed by Joe Borovich, an artist from Vancouver.

2. The highest number ever sported by a Canucks goaltender is 75, by Michael DiPietro during the 2019-20 season.

3. When the Canucks joined the NHL's first third jersey program, the team came up with a salmon-colored alternate featuring an off-center V and their "Flying Skate" logo.

4. Some high numbers have proven unpopular with Vancouver players. Nineteen numbers have gone unused in franchise history, as no Canuck has ever worn a jersey with the following numbers: 67, 68, 69, 74, 76, 78, 80, 84, 85, 86, 87, 90, 92, 93, 94, 95, 97, 98, or 99.

5. Star winger Markus Naslund wanted to wear number 19 when he was traded to the Canucks from Pittsburgh, since he had worn the number with his junior teams. Veteran Tim Hunter had the number, so Naslund had to sport 22 for a year. When Hunter left, Naslund switched to 19, which now hangs in the rafters at Rogers Arena to honor him.

6. Swedish twins Daniel and Henrik Sedin wore numbers 22 and 33 respectively during their tenure with the Canucks.

Daniel had been selected 2nd overall in the NHL Entry Draft, and Henrik was selected 3rd overall, so general manager Brian Burke suggested these numbers for the brothers.

7. Superstition may have scared some Canucks away from wearing the number 13. Only two players in franchise history have chosen to wear it for more than one season; Lars Lindgren from 1979-1984 and Artem Chubarov from 2000-2004.

8. The 1980s were a time of experimentation for Canucks uniforms. In addition to the bold orange, yellow, and black color scheme, the team also wore many patches, including commemorating Vancouver's centennial, the "Man in Motion" tour featuring Rick Hansen, and honoring Goodwill Ambassador Walter "Babe" Pratt.

9. Star winger Pavel Bure wanted to wear number 96 with Vancouver, to commemorate the day he came to North America from Russia (September 6, 1991). Canucks coach Pat Quinn believed that high numbers were a sign of showboating and assigned Bure number 10 instead. Bure did wear 96 for one season with the team, in 1996-97.

10. When the Canucks played in the 2014 Heritage Classic, they wore a maroon and white jersey with a V logo and the word "Vancouver" spelled out inside the V. This was done to pay homage to the city's original franchise, the Vancouver Millionaires.

CHAPTER 3:

CATCHY NICKNAMES

QUIZ TIME!

1. By which franchise nickname are the Canucks most commonly referred to?

   a. Orcas

   b. 'Nucks

   c. Coastals

   d. Pacifics

2. Vancouver winger Martin Gelinas is known as "The Eliminator" because of his penchant for scoring playoff series winning goals.

   a. True

   b. False

3. The longtime home of the Canucks, Rogers Arena, was formerly named General Motors Place, which is how it acquired which popular nickname?

   a. The Garage

   b. The Autobahn

c. The Hockey Factory

d. The Pacific Workshop

4. Which three forwards played together in a combination known as "The IKEA Line"?

   a. Mats Sundin, Henrik Sedin, and Loui Eriksson

   b. Ike Wilson, James Key, and Jonas Andersson

   c. Daniel Sedin, Henrik Sedin, and Markus Naslund

   d. Daniel Sedin, Elias Pettersson, and Oscar Fantenberg

5. Why was Canucks winger Pavel Bure nicknamed "The Russian Rocket"?

   a. His competitiveness reminded others of legendary Montreal Canadiens forward Maurice "Rocket" Richard.

   b. His tendency to leave the defensive zone and wait down ice for a breakout pass left him "alone in his own orbit down there."

   c. His shot accelerated so quickly that opposing goalies likened it to catching a rocket.

   d. His skating speed was so impressive that he was compared to a rocket taking off.

6. Which of the following is NOT a nickname that was given to Canucks center Mark Messier?

   a. Mess

   b. Double M

   c. Moose

   d. The Messiah

7. Despite never wearing the C for Vancouver, netminder Kirk McLean was known by the moniker "Captain Kirk."

    a. True
    b. False

8. Why was Loui Eriksson given the nickname "Little Things Loui" by sportswriter Jason Botchford?

    a. Despite his short stature (5'9"), he always delivered timely goals.
    b. He had a habit of collecting mementoes from opposing players after games and would ask for "any little thing."
    c. Coach Travis Green repeatedly mentioned in interviews that Eriksson paid attention to all the little details on the ice.
    d. Botchford felt that Eriksson could have become an NHL superstar if he just fixed "a few little things" in his game.

9. Which of the following is NOT a nickname that was given to Canucks defenseman Kevin Bieksa?

    a. Boom-Boom
    b. Stoneface
    c. The Sheriff
    d. Juice

10. For what reason did Canucks fans refer to goaltender Gary Smith as "Suitcase"?

    a. He was caught with adult magazines in his luggage during a customs check at the Vancouver airport.

b. His roommates said that after returning from road trips, he never bothered to unpack the clothes from his suitcase.

c. He played for seven different NHL teams throughout his long career.

d. When faced with high pressure situations, he "folded like a cheap suitcase."

11. Which Canucks player was known to fans and teammates by the nicknames "Mr. Sensitive" and "The Flow"?

a. Dana Murzyn

b. Bo Horvat

c. Alexandre Burrows

d. Brock Boeser

12. Defenseman Alex Edler was dubbed "Eagle" by Canucks teammate Trevor Linden through Linden's simple word association: "Edler. Eddie. Eddie the Eagle."

a. True

b. False

13. Which current Canuck is known to teammates by the nickname "Big Tuna"?

a. Elias Pettersson

b. Tyler Myers

c. Troy Stecher

d. Jake Virtanen

14. Why did teammate Brandon Sutter call Canucks defender Quinn Hughes by the nickname "Huggy Bear"?

a. Hughes dressed up as the character when he and some teammates used a Starsky and Hutch theme for a Halloween party.

b. It was a combination of his last name and a T-shirt Hughes wore with a picture of a bear on it.

c. Every time Sutter tried to drive to the net past Hughes in practice "he would wrap me up in a freaking bear hug."

d. After every Canucks victory, Hughes skates over to his goaltender and shares a hug before leaving the ice.

15. Which three speedy, United States born players comprised Vancouver's "American Express Line"?

a. David Booth, Ryan Kesler, and Chris Higgins

b. Trent Klatt, Brock Boeser, and Donald Brashear

c. Andrew Alberts, Reid Boucher, and Mike Brown

d. Jimmy Carson, Craig Coxe, and Dave Capuano

16. Canucks winger Todd Bertuzzi's nickname "Big Bert" was a play on words featuring his size, his last name, and a character from the popular children's show *Sesame Street*.

a. True

b. False

17. Why was the 2019 forward combination of Brock Boeser, Elias Pettersson, and J.T. Miller known as "The Lotto Line"?

a. All three had signed lucrative new contracts before the season, so they were said to have hit the jackpot.

b. Their games were based nearly all offensively, so putting the line on the ice was "as risky as playing the lottery."

c. Boeser wore number 6, Pettersson 40, and Miller 9, which mimicked the popular Canadian Lotto 649 sweepstakes.

d. Each of the three had been acquired with a lottery pick in the NHL Draft, and all had panned out well for the team.

18. Which respected Canucks forward was known as "The Professor" for his calm, calculated play and strategic thinking?

a. Jim Sandlak
b. Igor Larionov
c. Patrik Sundstrom
d. Andre Boudrias

19. One of the best forward lines in Canucks history was known as the "West Coast Express" because they were considered as unstoppable as a train roaring down the tracks. Which players were featured on this line?

a. Trevor Linden, Pavel Bure, and Alexander Mogilny
b. Daniel Sedin, Henrik Sedin, and Alexandre Burrows
c. Mark Messier, Trevor Linden, and Gino Odjick
d. Todd Bertuzzi, Brendan Morrison, and Markus Naslund

20. Thanks to his Native heritage and frequent fistfights on the ice, Canucks forward Gino Odjick was called "The Algonquin Enforcer."

    a. True
    b. False

QUIZ ANSWERS

1. B – 'Nucks

2. A – True

3. A – The Garage

4. C – Daniel Sedin, Henrik Sedin, and Markus Naslund

5. D – His skating speed was so impressive that he was compared to a rocket taking off.

6. B – Double M

7. A – True

8. C – Coach Travis Green repeatedly mentioned in interviews that Eriksson paid attention to all the little details on the ice.

9. B – Stoneface

10. C – He played for seven different NHL teams throughout his long career.

11. D – Brock Boeser

12. A – True

13. D – Jake Virtanen

14. B – It was a combination of his last name and a T-shirt Hughes wore with a picture of a bear on it.

15. A – David Booth, Ryan Kesler, and Chris Higgins

16. A – True

17. C – Boeser wore number 6, Pettersson 40, and Miller 9, which mimicked the popular Canadian Lotto 649 sweepstakes.

18. B – Igor Larionov

19. D – Todd Bertuzzi, Brendan Morrison, and Markus Naslund

20. A – True

DID YOU KNOW?

1. Vancouver's team nickname, "Canucks," derives from a slang term for Canadians. The term debuted in a political cartoon that originated in 1869, featuring a character named Johnny Canuck. Johnny served as a mascot for Vancouver's WHL team and is featured on the shoulders of the Canucks' alternate jersey.

2. Fiery Canucks coach John Tortorella picked up the nickname "The Paper Italian" while playing right wing at the University of Maine. As a bench boss, he was more commonly referred to by players and media as simply "Torts."

3. Vancouver netminder Gary Bromley was known as "Bones" thanks to the paint job on his goalie mask. Bromley wore a mask designed to look like a skull, which he hoped would strike fear into the hearts of opposing players.

4. During the 1970s and 1980s, the Canucks formed "The Kid Line," featuring Stan Smyl, Curt Fraser, and Thomas Gradin. The line was a major success, and Smyl went on to have his number retired by the club.

5. Franchise icon Trevor Linden played 16 seasons with Vancouver and showed great leadership along the way. He was nicknamed "Captain Canuck" for those reasons,

and because the name coincides with a famous Canadian comic book character.

6. When Daniel and Henrik Sedin skated with winger Jason King in 2003-04, some clever Vancouverites nicknamed the trio "The Mattress Line," because it featured two twins and a king.

7. Canucks forward Dave "Tiger" Williams earned his nickname through his fierceness on the ice. He recorded nearly 4,000 career penalty minutes, and although he celebrated goals by riding his stick like a witch on a broomstick, opponents did not often choose to challenge him for his exuberance.

8. Ryan Kesler, Pavol Demitra, and Mats Sundin lent their first initials to the Canucks' high-powered "RPM Line," although Demitra's and Sundin's advanced age meant that the line was short-lived.

9. For two straight seasons, the Canucks had been eliminated by the Chicago Blackhawks in the postseason. In the third year, the Canucks took a 3-0 series lead before Chicago came back to tie the series and force a Game 7. In Game 7, Vancouver winger Alex Burrows scored two goals, including the overtime winner, and was forever after known as "The Dragon Slayer."

10. Canucks defenseman Ed Jovanovski was so solid and reliable while patrolling the blue line that he was given the nickname "JovoCop," a takeoff on the popular movie *Robocop*, which featured a futuristic police robot who could perform above and beyond regular cops.

CHAPTER 4:

THE CAPTAIN CLASS

QUIZ TIME!

1. Which player was honored by being named the inaugural captain of the Vancouver Canucks in 1970?

    a. Right winger Stan Smyl

    b. Left winger Andre Boudrias

    c. Right winger Tiger Williams

    d. Center Orland Kurtenbach

2. The Canucks have never named a Russian player as even an assistant captain, let alone a captain.

    a. True

    b. False

3. Which captain holds the record for most points in a season while leading the Canucks, with 104?

    a. Trevor Linden

    b. Henrik Sedin

    c. Markus Naslund

    d. Pavel Bure

4. Who was the first Canucks captain to lead the team to a Stanley Cup Final?

   a. Don Lever
   b. Kevin McCarthy
   c. Stan Smyl
   d. Orland Kurtenbach

5. For how many consecutive seasons did captain Kevin McCarthy wear the C and lead all Canucks defensemen in scoring?

   a. 2
   b. 3
   c. 6
   d. 8

6. Which player was the oldest to wear the C for the Vancouver Canucks, at 39 years old?

   a. Henrik Sedin
   b. Orland Kurtenbach
   c. Mark Messier
   d. Markus Naslund

7. In their entire history, the Vancouver Canucks have never named a goaltender captain of the team.

   a. True
   b. False

8. Which early Canucks captain set the team record with 62 assists during the 1974-75 season; a mark which stood for 32 years?

a. Andre Boudrias

b. Orland Kurtenbach

c. Don Lever

d. Chris Oddleifson

9. Which Canuck set the franchise record for most penalty minutes in a season by a Vancouver captain?

a. Trevor Linden

b. Kevin McCarthy

c. Stan Smyl

d. Mark Messier

10. Left winger Don Lever recorded the lowest plus/minus season for any Vancouver captain in 1978-79. How low did he finish?

a. -12

b. -26

c. -35

d. -43

11. How many times did prolific Canucks captain Markus Naslund score 40 (or more) goals in a single season?

a. 1

b. 2

c. 3

d. 5

12. For three seasons in the 1980s, Vancouver elected not to name a captain. Instead, they had a rotation of players wear an A (usually designated for assistant captains) with three sporting the letter in each game.

a. True

b. False

13. Which captain did the Canucks trade to the New York Islanders to complete a deal in which they received Todd Bertuzzi, Bryan McCabe, and a draft pick (which became Jarkko Ruutu) in return?

a. Trevor Linden

b. Roberto Luongo

c. Mark Messier

d. Doug Lidster

14. How many players that have held the Canucks captaincy have been elected to the Hockey Hall of Fame?

a. 0

b. 1

c. 3

d. 7

15. In which year did the Canucks name their first captain who was not born in Canada?

a. 1970

b. 1980

c. 1990

d. 2000

16. During their entire history, the Vancouver Canucks have only elected two defensemen to be the captain of the team.

a. True

b. False

17. One Canucks captain has played for eight NHL teams, more than any other franchise leader. Who was this well-travelled player?

    a. Stan Smyl
    b. Doug Lidster
    c. Mark Messier
    d. Dan Quinn

18. Which Canuck was the youngest player in the team's history to be made captain, at the age of 20?

    a. Dan Quinn
    b. Kevin McCarthy
    c. Trevor Linden
    d. Bo Horvat

19. The team has had some great leaders who were never given the formal responsibility of being the Canucks' captain. Which of these players is the only one to wear the C?

    a. Daniel Sedin
    b. Tony Tanti
    c. Markus Naslund
    d. Ed Jovanovski

20. In Trevor Linden and Henrik Sedin, the Canucks boast the two longest-serving captains (measured by seasons played while captain of the team) in NHL history.

    a. True
    b. False

QUIZ ANSWERS

1. D – Center Orland Kurtenbach

2. B – False

3. C – Markus Naslund

4. B – Kevin McCarthy

5. B – 3

6. C – Mark Messier

7. B – False

8. A – Andre Boudrias

9. C – Stan Smyl

10. D – -43

11. C – 3

12. B – False

13. A – Trevor Linden

14. B – 1

15. D – 2000

16. A – True

17. D – Dan Quinn

18. C – Trevor Linden

19. C – Markus Naslund

20. B – False

DID YOU KNOW?

1. Canucks goaltender Roberto Luongo held the team's captaincy for two seasons between 2008-10. Prior to this, the last NHL goalie to be named a team's captain was Bill Durnan of the Montreal Canadiens, back in 1947-48.

2. Since NHL rules prohibited netminder Roberto Luongo from physically wearing the captain's C on his jersey, Luongo had a C painted on the chin of his goalie mask instead.

3. After center Henrik Sedin recorded a franchise record 112 points in 2009-10, goaltender Roberto Luongo gave up the captaincy to Sedin despite remaining on the team.

4. Two Canucks captains have played their entire NHL careers with Vancouver. Right winger Stan Smyl spent 13 seasons with the franchise, and center Henrik Sedin stayed with the team for all of his 17 years. Current captain, center Bo Horvat, has not played anywhere else in his 6-year NHL career, but it remains to be seen if he will retire as a Canuck.

5. For the Canucks, 1990-91 was an unusual year. Vancouver named three co-captains that year as a bit of a trial for three contenders for the position. Dan Quinn, Doug Lidster, and Trevor Linden all split the captaincy, with Linden suiting the role best and going on to claim it for many years afterward.

6. Canucks captain Stan Smyl was not afraid to demonstrate his leadership with rugged play when necessary. Amongst Vancouver captains, Smyl recorded the top five seasons with the highest penalty minutes recorded.

7. Many view center Mark Messier as the least popular captain in Vancouver history. Not only did Messier lead the hated New York Rangers to a Stanley Cup victory over the Canucks in 1994 before arriving in town, but he also caused the most popular captain in Vancouver history, Trevor Linden, to give up the C, which led to Linden being traded away from the club.

8. Franchise icon Stan Smyl has spent his entire career with the Canucks franchise. In addition to his time as captain on the ice, Smyl retired to become an assistant coach with the team, a head coach with their farm team, and also took positions in player development and scouting.

9. There was much criticism when the Canucks named left winger Markus Naslund captain in 2000. Many felt that Naslund (the first European captain in club history) did not have the leadership skills to serve in the role. Naslund proved his worth over the years, however, often leading the team in scoring and receiving votes for the Hart, Selke, Byng, and Pearson Trophies.

10. Long tenures with the franchise have been a tradition for many Canucks captains. Both Trevor Linden and Markus Naslund captained the team for 7 seasons, while Stan Smyl and Henrik Sedin led the way for 8.

CHAPTER 5:

STATISTICALLY SPEAKING

QUIZ TIME!

1. What is Vancouver's franchise record for most victories recorded by the club in a single regular season?

    a. 46 wins

    b. 51 wins

    c. 54 wins

    d. 60 wins

2. No one in Canucks history is within 200 assists of the Sedin twins at the top of Vancouver's record book.

    a. True

    b. False

3. Four goalies have recorded over 100 career wins for the Canucks. Which one of them has the most?

    a. Richard Brodeur

    b. Roberto Luongo

    c. Kirk McLean

    d. Dan Cloutier

4. Who was the Canucks' single-season leader in goals scored, with 60 tallies (accomplished twice)?

   a. Alexander Mogilny
   b. Stan Smyl
   c. Markus Naslund
   d. Pavel Bure

5. Which Canuck really made his shots count, showing his accuracy with the highest career shooting percentage for the team (with a minimum of 400 shots taken)?

   a. Mike Walton
   b. Elias Pettersson
   c. Petr Nedved
   d. Darcy Rota

6. The most recorded penalty minutes in any season by a Canucks player is 372. Who spent enough time in the penalty box to establish this club record?

   a. Donald Brashear
   b. Gino Odjick
   c. Garth Butcher
   d. Tiger Williams

7. During the 1980-81 season, the Canucks finished 25% of their regular season games in a tie.

   a. True
   b. False

8. Which goaltender holds the Vancouver record for most wins in a single season, with 47 victories posted?

a. Kirk McLean

b. Dan Cloutier

c. Roberto Luongo

d. Gary Smith

9. Which Canuck has played more NHL games with the franchise than any other player?

a. Henrik Sedin

b. Alexander Edler

c. Trevor Linden

d. Daniel Sedin

10. The talented Daniel Sedin is Vancouver's all-time leader in goals scored. How many times did the left winger score a goal for the team?

a. 288

b. 317

c. 393

d. 481

11. Who holds the single-season Canucks record for points per game, at 1.41?

a. Stan Smyl

b. Daniel Sedin

c. Henrik Sedin

d. Pavel Bure

12. Center Mats Sundin, obtained late in his career as a mentor to fellow Swedes Daniel and Henrik Sedin, led by example and scored more goals than anyone on the team during his short tenure with Vancouver.

a. True

b. False

13. Which Canucks defenseman has recorded the most points while playing with the club?

   a. Mattias Ohlund

   b. Alexander Edler

   c. Dennis Kearns

   d. Jyrki Lumme

14. On the Canucks' top 10 list for points scored by a player in a season, how many times does Pavel Bure's name appear?

   a. 3 times

   b. 5 times

   c. 6 times

   d. 8 times

15. How many Canucks have fired over 2,000 shots on net for the club during their careers?

   a. 0

   b. 2

   c. 3

   d. 6

16. Defenseman Christian Ehrhoff and left winger Daniel Sedin both posted a +36 rating during the 2009-10 season, which remains a franchise record.

   a. True

   b. False

17. Which Canucks center recorded the highest career plus/minus with the team, posting a +165?

    a. Cliff Ronning
    b. Ryan Kesler
    c. Igor Larionov
    d. Henrik Sedin

18. Which Canuck recorded the most game-winning goals for the team, scoring 86 clutch markers to claim victory for the squad?

    a. Daniel Sedin
    b. Tony Tanti
    c. Trevor Linden
    d. Alexandre Burrows

19. Which two teammates posted the highest combined point total in a season for the Canucks?

    a. Daniel Sedin and Henrik Sedin in 2010-11
    b. Markus Naslund and Todd Bertuzzi in 2002-03
    c. Pavel Bure and Alexander Mogilny in 1996-97
    d. Patrik Sundstrom and Tony Tanti in 1983-84

20. Goalie Roberto Luongo's 2006-07 season is the benchmark in terms of shots faced, as he faced 2,169; the only time a Canucks goaltender has seen more than 2,100 shots in a season.

    a. True
    b. False

QUIZ ANSWERS

1. C – 54 wins

2. A – True

3. B – Roberto Luongo

4. D – Pavel Bure

5. D – Darcy Rota

6. A – Donald Brashear

7. A – True

8. C – Roberto Luongo

9. A – Henrik Sedin

10. C – 393

11. D – Pavel Bure

12. B – False

13. B – Alexander Edler

14. A – 3 times

15. C – 3

16. A – True

17. D – Henrik Sedin

18. A – Daniel Sedin

19. B – Markus Naslund and Todd Bertuzzi in 2002-03

20. A – True

DID YOU KNOW?

1. Two players have scored more than 1,000 points with the Canucks franchise. Twins Daniel and Henrik Sedin are closely tied together with Vancouver, joining the team the same year, retiring in the same year, and establishing many club records together. Henrik finished atop the leaderboard with 1,070 career points, and Daniel was not far behind with 1,041.

2. Former Canucks icon Pavel Bure ranks 23rd on the all-time list for most points per game in the NHL, with 1.110. He ranks just below Gilbert Perreault, who the Canucks missed out on in their inaugural draft lottery. Other Canucks to score more than a point per game include Mark Messier, Alexander Mogilny, and Mats Sundin.

3. Not counting seasons shortened by a lockout, the 2010-11 Canucks were the stingiest version of the club to ever take the ice. They allowed only 185 goals against during the entire 82-game regular season.

4. Speedy winger Pavel Bure was a force on the penalty kill for the Canucks, scoring a team record 24 short-handed goals during his career, including 7 markers with a man down in 1992-93 alone (also a team single-season record).

5. A few Vancouver forwards often scored in bunches. Three players—Pavel Bure, Markus Naslund, and Tony Tanti— recorded 10 hat tricks (scoring three goals in the same

game); during their careers, Bure and Tanti each scored 4 goals in a single game once, and Naslund achieved that mark twice. No Canuck has ever scored 5 goals in a game.

6. Vancouver right winger Gino Odjick leads the franchise with 2,127 career penalty minutes for the team. In a single season protecting the Canucks (1996-97), he racked up 371 penalty minutes, which was more than he recorded in the next 5 years combined while playing for the New York Islanders and Philadelphia Flyers.

7. Kirk McLean dominates the Canucks' record books for goaltenders. He leads the franchise in: games played, losses, ties plus overtime or shootout losses, goals against, shots against, saves, and minutes played.

8. The most recent time the Canucks scored more than 300 goals in a season was 1992-93, when they tallied 346. This remains the team record; although, they did also crack 300 in two consecutive seasons early in the 1980s.

9. The deadliest Canuck on the power play was Daniel Sedin. He scored a team record 138 goals with the man advantage, 24 more than another Swedish left winger who played for the club, Markus Naslund.

10. In 1992-93, Pavel Bure fired 407 shots on net, establishing the Vancouver record for most shots taken by one player in a single season and leading the league that year. He scored 60 times, which put him 5th in the NHL behind Teemu Selanne, Alexander Mogilny, Mario Lemieux, and Luc Robitaille.

CHAPTER 6:

THE TRADE MARKET

QUIZ TIME!

1. The very first player-for-player trade ever made by the Vancouver Canucks occurred in the summer of 1970, when the Canucks received winger Andre Hinse from the Toronto Maple Leafs. Which players did they give up in return?

    a. John Arbour and George Gardner
    b. Pat Hannigan and Ted McCaskill
    c. Marc Reaume and Ted Taylor
    d. Murray Hall and Jocelyn Guevremont

2. The Canucks once completed a trade with the Anaheim Ducks sending forward Peter Zezel there for future considerations, but the trade was nullified after Zezel refused to report to Anaheim.

    a. True
    b. False

3. In 2001, the Canucks made a trade with the Washington Capitals to re-obtain former captain Trevor Linden. How many more seasons did Linden play in his second stint with the team?

   a. 1
   b. 2
   c. 4
   d. 6

4. The Vancouver Canucks twice traded for winger Brad May, once giving up a player and once giving up a draft pick. Which teams did they pick up May from?

   a. Anaheim Ducks and Toronto Maple Leafs
   b. Buffalo Sabres and Arizona Coyotes
   c. Colorado Avalanche and Arizona Coyotes
   d. Buffalo Sabres and Toronto Maple Leafs

5. Which useful Canucks player was NOT received from the St. Louis Blues in 1991 in exchange for Garth Butcher and Dan Quinn?

   a. Sergio Momesso
   b. Cliff Ronning
   c. Petri Skriko
   d. Geoff Courtnall

6. One of the Canucks' best trades saw them acquire future captain Markus Naslund in exchange for forward Alek Stojanov. Which team regretted making that deal with Vancouver?

a. Buffalo Sabres

b. New Jersey Devils

c. Columbus Blue Jackets

d. Pittsburgh Penguins

7. Vancouver has completed more trades with the San Jose Sharks than with any other NHL franchise.

   a. True

   b. False

8. In what year did the Canucks first make a trade for "future considerations"?

   a. 1971

   b. 1974

   c. 1979

   d. 1983

9. In 1996, Vancouver brought two heavyweight enforcers to the team in separate trades. Which two fighters did they trade for?

   a. Chris Simon and Bob Probert

   b. Basil McRae and Tie Domi

   c. Stu Grimson and Shane Churla

   d. Joey Kocur and Donald Brashear

10. Who did the Vancouver Canucks select with the first draft pick acquired by the team, an 8th round choice in the 1971 NHL Entry Draft?

    a. Forward Bob Murphy

    b. Defenseman Pat Quinn

    c. Goalie John Garrett

    d. Forward Phil Maloney

11. In 1998, the Canucks traded longtime netminder Kirk McLean. They received another goalie in return, only to flip the new goalie for a third puck stopper. Which players did they obtain to play between the pipes?

    a. Steve Weeks, then Felix Potvin

    b. Bob Essensa, then Arturs Irbe

    c. Sean Burke, then Garth Snow

    d. Glen Hanlon, then Kay Whitmore

12. Vancouver has never in its history completed a trade with the Detroit Red Wings.

    a. True

    b. False

13. Who did the Canucks send to the Philadelphia Flyers when they traded for future captain Kevin McCarthy in 1978?

    a. Michel Petit and Ron Sedlbauer

    b. Gerry O'Flaherty

    c. Bob Dailey and Rick Blight

    d. Dennis Ververgaert

14. Canucks goaltender Dunc Wilson was traded in 1973 and returned to Vancouver in another trade in 1978. Which NHL team(s) did he play for in between his stints with the Canucks?

    a. Chicago Blackhawks

    b. Minnesota North Stars and Philadelphia Flyers

c. Toronto Maple Leafs, New York Rangers, and Pittsburgh Penguins

d. Buffalo Sabres, New Jersey Devils, Detroit Red Wings, and Boston Bruins

15. In October of 1989, the Canucks acquired defenseman Rod Buskas from the Pittsburgh Penguins. How long did he remain with Vancouver before being traded back to Pittsburgh?

a. 2.5 months

b. 3 seasons

c. 5 seasons

d. 10 seasons

16. In 1990, Vancouver made a trade with the St. Louis Blues in which each team received a 2nd round pick that would be used on a player named Craig.

a. True

b. False

17. Which high-scoring right winger did the Canucks pluck from the Chicago Blackhawks in a 1983 trade that saw them give up left winger Curt Fraser?

a. Tony Tanti

b. Petrik Skriko

c. Rich Sutter

d. Jim Sandlak

18. In 1993, Vancouver acquired a player from the Washington Capitals who shared a name with which television sitcom character that was popular at the time?

a. Al Bundy

b. Tim Taylor

c. Sam Malone

d. Dan Connor

19. In the span of less than two years, the Canucks made trades with the New Jersey Devils and Edmonton Oilers to acquire which two players?

a. Brent Sutter and Rich Sutter

b. Patrik Sundstrom and Tomas Sandstrom

c. Michael Stevens and Steven Michaels

d. Greg D. Adams and Greg C. Adams

20. Canucks forwards, and twin brothers, Daniel and Henrik Sedin did not have no-trade clauses in their contracts but did have a clause that stated if one was traded, the other had to be dealt to the same team as well.

a. True

b. False

QUIZ ANSWERS

1. B – Pat Hannigan and Ted McCaskill

2. A – True

3. D – 6

4. B – Buffalo Sabres and Arizona Coyotes

5. C – Petri Skriko

6. D – Pittsburgh Penguins

7. B – False

8. B – 1974

9. D – Joey Kocur and Donald Brashear

10. A – Forward Bob Murphy

11. C – Sean Burke, then Garth Snow

12. B – False

13. D – Dennis Ververgaert

14. C – Toronto Maple Leafs, New York Rangers, and Pittsburgh Penguins

15. A – 2.5 months

16. A – True

17. A – Tony Tanti

18. B – Tim Taylor

19. D – Greg D. Adams and Greg C. Adams

20. B – False

DID YOU KNOW?

1. Vancouver's first two NHL trades occurred on June 10, 1970. The Canucks agreed not to select specific players from the Pittsburgh Penguins in the expansion draft and, in return, were given an 8th round pick that they used to select Bob Murphy. The Canucks also sent 7th and 9th round picks to the St. Louis Blues and received center Andre Boudrias, who would eventually go on to become the team's captain

2. During their history, the Canucks have traded for some famous Hall of Fame names. Unfortunately, they did not get the players who made the names famous. Vancouver has dealt for not quite superstars Fedor (not Sergei) Fedorov, Mike (not Luc) Robitaille, Richard (not Martin) Brodeur, and Sean (not Chris) Pronger.

3. The Canucks acquired a star goaltender in 2006 as part of a trade with the Florida Panthers, primarily giving up Todd Bertuzzi in the deal. When Luongo had to be moved again due to contract concerns in 2014, the team shipped him out...back to the Florida Panthers. This time, Vancouver picked up goalie Jacob Markstrom in return.

4. Fellow expansion teams Vancouver and Buffalo have a rich history of trades throughout the years. Significant names moved between the two teams include: Jerry Korab, Mike Robitaille, Michael Peca, Jay McKee, Alexander

Mogilny, Geoff Sanderson, Brad May, Mika Noronen, Steve Bernier, Cody Hodgson, and Zack Kassian.

5. Vancouver has never completed a three-team trade, but general manager Brian Burke did do some intense maneuvering on June 25 and 26, 1999, completing three separate trades with the Atlanta Thrashers, Chicago Blackhawks, and Tampa Bay Lightning that left Vancouver in position to draft both Sedin twins in the NHL Entry Draft.

6. Though he never played a game for the team, the Canucks maximized their return for winger Andre Hinse. Vancouver acquired Hinse from Toronto in August of 1970 for two players. Knowing Toronto was fond of him, in September of 1970, the Canucks loaned him back to the Leafs for cash. Then, in September of 1971, they traded him to the Leafs for good and received center Doug Brindley in return.

7. One of the worst trades made by the Canucks occurred in 1986 when they sent rugged winger Cam Neely and a 3rd overall draft pick to the Boston Bruins for center Barry Pederson. Pederson was not terrible for the Canucks, but Neely became a Hall of Famer with the Bruins, and the 3rd pick was used on defenseman Glen Wesley, who played in almost 1,500 NHL games.

8. The seven goaltenders who have played the most career games with Vancouver have all been acquired in trades. Kirk McLean, Roberto Luongo, Richard Brodeur, Jacob

Markstrom, Dan Cloutier, Gary Smith, and Ryan Miller were all drafted by other franchises.

9. Forward Mike Sillinger holds the NHL record for most trades, as he was included in nine separate deals during his career. Vancouver was involved in two of those, acquiring Sillinger from Anaheim for Roman Oksiuta in 1996, and sending him to Philadelphia for a draft pick in 1998.

10. The largest trade (by number of assets) ever completed by the Canucks was consummated in 1999 with the Florida Panthers. Vancouver acquired Mike Brown, Ed Jovanovski, Kevin Weekes, Dave Gagner, and a 1st round draft pick, while giving up Pavel Bure, Bret Hedican, Brad Ference, and a 3rd round draft pick.

CHAPTER 7:

DRAFT DAY

QUIZ TIME!

1. When the city of Vancouver hosted the NHL Entry Draft in 2019, which prospect did the Canucks draft with their 1st round pick in front of the hometown fans?

    a. Right winger Cole Caufield

    b. Left winger Matthew Boldy

    c. Defenseman Philip Broberg

    d. Right winger Vasily Podkolzin

2. The Canucks have never held the 1st overall pick in the NHL Draft in the 50-year history of the franchise.

    a. True

    b. False

3. How high did Vancouver select defenseman Olli Juolevi in the 2016 NHL Entry Draft?

    a. 1st round, 5th overall

    b. 2nd round, 43rd overall

c. 4th round, 114th overall

d. 7th round, 222nd overall

4. Which goaltender did the Canucks select highest in the NHL Entry Draft, using a 25th overall pick to add the netminder to their team?

   a. Cory Schneider from Andover

   b. Thatcher Demko from Boston College

   c. Troy Gamble from Medicine Hat

   d. Ed Dyck from Calgary

5. Who was the first-ever player selected by the Canucks in the NHL Entry Draft?

   a. Defenseman Jim Hargreaves

   b. Defenseman Dale Tallon

   c. Defenseman Jocelyn Guevremont

   d. Left winger Don Lever

6. Which player, drafted by the Canucks, went on to score the most NHL points for another team?

   a. Center Igor Larionov

   b. Center Michael Peca

   c. Right winger Cam Neely

   d. Right winger Rick Vaive

7. Vancouver has drafted precisely eight players who have played a single game in the NHL, none of whom recorded a goal.

   a. True

   b. False

8. The Canucks have mined the WHL for talent frequently in the NHL Entry Draft and have selected 13 players from one specific WHL location, more than they have chosen from any other franchise. Which team was it?

    a. Brandon Wheat Kings
    b. Kamloops Blazers
    c. Medicine Hat Tigers
    d. Calgary Centennials/Wranglers/Hitmen

9. Fan favorite Trevor Linden was selected in the 1st round by the Vancouver Canucks in 1988. Which junior league did he play in?

    a. Quebec Major Junior Hockey League
    b. Western Hockey League
    c. Ontario Hockey League
    d. American Hockey League

10. Who was the first player ever drafted by the Canucks that did not play for a Canadian junior team?

    a. Right winger Norm Cherry
    b. Center Cliff Ronning
    c. Center Ryan Kesler
    d. Right winger Petri Skriko

11. The Vegas Golden Knights selected which Vancouver Canuck, who went on to play just 42 games for the Golden Knights, in the 2017 Expansion Draft?

    a. Right winger Zack Kassian
    b. Left winger Sven Baertschi

c. Defenseman Luca Sbisa

d. Goaltender Eddie Lack

12. First round Canucks pick Quinn Hughes went 7th overall in 2018 but does not have family bragging rights because he has a brother who was drafted in the NHL as well, with the 1st overall pick.

a. True

b. False

13. The Canucks struck out mightily in the 1976 NHL Draft, selecting seven skaters who scored a total of how many NHL goals?

a. 47

b. 85

c. 112

d. 186

14. When the Canucks joined the NHL in 1970, they participated in a draft lottery with fellow expansion team Buffalo Sabres to decide who would choose first in the expansion and entry drafts, with Buffalo winning both. How were these lotteries conducted?

a. Sealed envelopes with the team names inside were drawn out of a box.

b. Numbered Ping-Pong balls were sucked out of a clear cage.

c. A roulette-style wheel was spun in front of team representatives.

d. A coin with the team logos on each side was flipped by the league president.

15. Excellent Czech center Petr Nedved was drafted by Vancouver 2nd overall in the 1990 NHL Entry Draft. Which even better winger was selected one spot ahead of him?

    a. Keith Primeau, by the Detroit Red Wings
    b. Keith Tkachuk, by the Winnipeg Jets
    c. Jaromir Jagr, by the Pittsburgh Penguins
    d. Owen Nolan, by the Quebec Nordiques

16. After signing youngster Bill Derlago to an illegal, underage contract in 1978, the Canucks were caught and forced to forfeit 3 draft picks the following year.

    a. True
    b. False

17. Up to and including the 2019 NHL Entry Draft, how many player selections have the Vancouver Canucks made in their history?

    a. 308
    b. 396
    c. 435
    d. 512

18. Which position has Vancouver traditionally put a premium on, by drafting it most frequently when they've held a top 10 overall draft pick?

    a. Defense
    b. Left wing

c. Center

d. Right wing

19. What is the lowest position in the draft that the Canucks have selected a player who would go on to make the Hockey Hall of Fame (Igor Larionov in 1985)?

a. 88th overall pick

b. 107th overall pick

c. 163rd overall pick

d. 214th overall pick

20. Taking Daniel and Henrik Sedin with the 2nd and 3rd overall picks in 1999 is the only time the Canucks have ever made back-to-back selections in the NHL Draft.

a. True

b. False

QUIZ ANSWERS

1. D – Right winger Vasily Podkolzin

2. A – True

3. A – 1st round, 5th overall

4. C – Troy Gamble from Medicine Hat

5. B – Defenseman Dale Tallon

6. D – Right winger Rick Vaive

7. A – True

8. D – Calgary Centennials/Wranglers/Hitmen

9. B – Western Hockey League

10. A – Right winger Norm Cherry

11. C – Defenseman Luca Sbisa

12. A – True

13. A – 47

14. C – A roulette-style wheel was spun in front of team representatives.

15. D – Owen Nolan, by the Quebec Nordiques

16. B – False

17. C – 435

18. A – Defense

19. D – 214th overall pick

20. B – False

DID YOU KNOW?

1. Between 1987 and 1994, Vancouver enjoyed a stretch in which they selected at least one player per year who lasted 700 games in the NHL. During those years, they hit on: Garry Valk, Trevor Linden, Pavel Bure, Petr Nedved, Jassen Cullimore, Adrian Aucoin, Michael Peca, Scott Walker, and Mattias Ohlund.

2. The Canucks were early to jump into the talent pool of Russia and Eastern Europe in the draft. They took chances by selecting top players years before many other teams dared (Igor Larionov and Robert Kron in 1985, Vladimir Krutov in 1986, Pavel Bure in 1989).

3. In 1991, the Canucks drafted right winger Alek Stojanov 7th overall. Stojanov matched his draft position, scoring exactly 7 NHL points. Luckily, Vancouver was able to trade Stojanov for Markus Naslund, who tallied 869 points in the NHL.

4. The Canucks have drafted four players who played for Vancouver's team in the WCHL: center Brian Shmyr in 1975, center Stu Ostlund in 1976, goalie Richard Martens in 1978, and left winger Tim Lorentz in 1983. Unfortunately, none of the four ever made it into an NHL game.

5. The first Canucks draft pick who went on to play 1,000 NHL games was left winger Don Lever. Vancouver selected him 3rd overall out of Niagara Falls in the 1972

Entry Draft. Lever starred for the team for eight years and went on to play eight more for five other NHL teams as well.

6. Swedish twins Daniel and Henrik Sedin sit in the top two positions for assists amongst any Canucks draft picks. Combined, the two have 1,478 career helpers. Vancouver has drafted approximately two dozen other Swedish players, but even adding all their assists together would not match the Sedins' total.

7. The largest Canucks draft class ever was selected in 1984, when the team drafted 14 players over the course of the draft. It was not exactly a stellar class, however. Eight of the players selected, including the lone goalie, Rex Grant, never made it to the NHL. Five others appeared in less than a full season's worth of games during their careers. The only success story was top pick J.J. Daigneault, who was a stalwart on defense for nearly 900 NHL games.

8. Vancouver has drafted four players who went on to record over 2,000 penalty minutes in the NHL. Ron Stern and Harold Snepsts were taken in the 4th round. Gino Odjick was a 5th rounder. The outlier was defenseman Garth Butcher, who was drafted 10th overall in the 1st round.

9. The Canucks drafted two goalies in 1977. Murray Bannerman and Glen Hanlon both played over 250 NHL games. Only one of the more than 40 other goalies drafted by Vancouver has met that threshold (Cory Schneider in 2004).

10. The latest picks the Canucks have made in the NHL Draft were in 2003 and 2004. In 2003, they selected defenseman Matthew Hansen with the 285th overall pick. In 2004, they chose left winger Jannik Hansen with the 287th overall pick. Although Matthew never made it in the NHL, Jannik incredibly defied the odds to play over 500 games with Vancouver.

CHAPTER 8:

GOALTENDER TIDBITS

QUIZ TIME!

1. How many goalies started for Vancouver during the team's challenging first season in the NHL?

   a. 1

   b. 2

   c. 3

   d. 7

2. Vancouver goalie Corey Hirsch won a silver medal at the Winter Olympics after allowing a shootout goal to Sweden's Peter Forsberg. The goal was commemorated with a postage stamp in Sweden, but it featured a generic goaltender because the competitive Hirsch refused to allow himself to be shown on it.

   a. True

   b. False

3. Which goaltender has recorded the most career shutouts while with the Vancouver Canucks?

a. Dan Cloutier

b. Kirk McLean

c. Richard Brodeur

d. Roberto Luongo

4. Which Vancouver netminder is perhaps known better for his post-playing career in the broadcasting booth, both for Hockey Night in Canada and for Canucks games on Sportsnet?

a. Gary Bromley

b. John Garrett

c. Kirk McLean

d. Eddie Lack

5. During the 1983 All-Star Game, which Vancouver goalie was announced as the MVP before the game ended, only to see the award revoked and given to Wayne Gretzky after Gretzky scored four goals in the final ten minutes?

a. Glen Hanlon

b. Richard Brodeur

c. John Garrett

d. Bob Essensa

6. Which of the following is NOT a true fact about quirky Canucks goaltender Gary Smith?

a. He often brought his pet dog, Rinkrat, to Canucks practices to watch from the bench.

b. He inspired the NHL rule prohibiting goalies from skating past the red line.

c. He once left Pacific Coliseum without changing out of his goaltending uniform.

d. He once punted the puck in a game, almost hitting the clock at Maple Leaf Gardens.

7. It is a Canucks tradition for every goaltender to tap both posts and the crossbar with his stick following the warm-up before a game.

a. True

b. False

8. 8. From which injury did Canucks goalie Roberto Luongo heroically return to record a shutout against the Montreal Canadiens on his first day discharged from the intensive care unit of the hospital?

a. A deep cut on his glove wrist caused by the skate blade of an opposing player

b. A herniated disc in his back caused by a collision while playing the puck behind his net

c. A concussion caused by a player falling on his head during a pileup in the crease

d. A damaged windpipe caused by a teammate's shot hitting his throat in practice

9. Which Canucks goaltender holds the franchise record for most saves recorded in a shutout, with 49 stops?

a. Roberto Luongo

b. Dan Cloutier

c. Jacob Markstrom

d. Gary Smith

10. Longtime Canucks netminder Kirk McLean recorded his first NHL shutout against which NHL team?

    a. Detroit Red Wings
    b. Pittsburgh Penguins
    c. New Jersey Devils
    d. Boston Bruins

11. Goaltenders Kirk McLean and Roberto Luongo have taken the Canucks as deep as they have ever gone into the playoffs: Game 7 of the Stanley Cup Finals. Against which opponents did these two square-off in the Finals?

    a. New York Rangers and Boston Bruins
    b. New York Islanders and Pittsburgh Penguins
    c. New Jersey Devils and Tampa Bay Lightning
    d. Philadelphia Flyers and Ottawa Senators

12. Canucks goalie Ryan Miller has at least one victory against every team in the NHL.

    a. True
    b. False

13. Who was the Canucks goaltender quoted as saying "I created a monster" after allowing superstar Wayne Gretzky's first-ever NHL goal?

    a. Richard Brodeur
    b. Cesare Maniago
    c. John Garrett
    d. Glen Hanlon

14. Which two goaltenders, both of whom would play for the Canucks, dueled in the 2010 Winter Olympics men's ice hockey gold medal game?

    a. Ryan Miller and Jacob Markstrom
    b. Cory Schneider and Roberto Luongo
    c. Roberto Luongo and Ryan Miller
    d. Jacob Markstrom and Roberto Luongo

15. During the 2000-01 NHL season, the Canucks' crease was crowded with 3 NHL quality goaltenders. Which of the following did NOT play for them between the pipes that year?

    a. Bob Essensa
    b. Garth Snow
    c. Dan Cloutier
    d. Felix Potvin

16. Former Canucks goalie Gary Bromley was the first goaltender in professional hockey to score a goal.

    a. True
    b. False

17. Vancouver went through how many goaltenders in the 7.5 years between Kirk McLean's departure and Roberto Luongo's arrival, leading general manager Brian Burke to invent the term "goalie graveyard"?

    a. 8
    b. 12
    c. 15
    d. 18

18. Vancouver goaltender Arturs Irbe played in the 2002 and 2006 Winter Olympics for which team?

    a. Russia
    b. Germany
    c. Switzerland
    d. Latvia

19. Canucks legend Kirk McLean became a thoroughbred owner in his retirement and co-owned a horse that won the 136th running of the Queen's Plate. What was his horse's name?

    a. Stanley
    b. Regal Discovery
    c. Vancouver Delight
    d. Butterfly Style

20. Canucks goalie Cory Schneider was born and raised in the United States of America but holds Swiss citizenship because of his family ancestry.

    a. True
    b. False

QUIZ ANSWERS

1. C – 3

2. A – True

3. D – Roberto Luongo

4. B – John Garrett

5. C – John Garrett

6. A – He often brought his pet dog, Rinkrat, to Canucks practices to watch from the bench.

7. B – False

8. D – A damaged windpipe caused by a teammate's shot hitting his throat in practice

9. C – Jacob Markstrom

10. B – Pittsburgh Penguins

11. A – New York Rangers and Boston Bruins

12. A – True

13. D – Glen Hanlon

14. C – Roberto Luongo and Ryan Miller

15. B – Garth Snow

16. B – False

17. D – 18

18. D – Latvia

19. B – Regal Discovery

20. A – True

DID YOU KNOW?

1. During the Canucks' first season, veteran goalie Charlie Hodge (age 37) and youngster Dunc Wilson (age 32) both started 35 games for the team. Hodge fared decently, with a 15-13-5 record, but Wilson ended the year an awful 3-25-2.

2. Vancouver netminder Corey Hirsch was open about his difficulties with his mental health. He once described his goalie mask design as "the perfect representation of what was going on inside my head." The mask had a silhouette of director Alfred Hitchcock, pictures of the Bates house from Hitchcock's movie Psycho, and a blood red and orange sky.

3. Canucks goaltender Richard Brodeur owns the dubious honor of allowing the most goals by Wayne Gretzky throughout The Great One's career. Gretzky found the back of the net 29 times against Brodeur.

4. Vancouver's Ryan Miller actually started in hockey as a forward. When he begged his father to let him become a goalie, his dad made him a deal: score two goals and add three assists in the next game, and Miller could play net with a new catching glove from his dad. Miller did exactly that, and his goaltending career was launched.

5. One of the hottest starts in Canucks history was driven by goalie Dan Cloutier in 2002. He recorded the first-ever

opening game shutout for the franchise, over the Calgary Flames, and won a team record 10 straight games in November before two knee injuries sidetracked his season.

6. Post-retirement, ex Canucks goalie Dunc Wilson sued the team, claiming that they improperly treated a mole. The mole was actually skin cancer and required complicated removal surgery, which Wilson claimed ended his career early.

7. No goalies who have played for the Canucks have been enshrined in the Hall of Fame. However, Roberto Luongo, who starred for the team from 2006-2014, will likely be elected when he is eligible in 2022 as he retired with the third most wins of all time, 489.

8. Canucks goalie Ryan Miller was named to the United States Olympic men's ice hockey team three times, in 2006, 2010, and 2014. He did not play in 2006 but was declared the most valuable player of the tournament in 2010, when he helped the Americans to a silver medal.

9. Goaltender Kirk McLean's mask made use of the Canucks' "Flying V" design, copied from their earlier jerseys. McLean used a tri-color gold, black, and red V on both the forehead and chin of his popular mask.

10. Canucks netminder Frank Caprice also played goalie for the Vancouver Voodoo of Roller Hockey International, in 1993, before finishing his ice hockey career in Italy and Britain.

CHAPTER 9:

ON THE BLUE LINE

QUIZ TIME!

1. Finnish Canucks defenseman Sami Salo has won three Olympic medals in men's ice hockey during his career. Which medals were they?

   a. 2 golds and 1 bronze
   b. 3 silvers
   c. 1 gold, 1 silver, and 1 bronze
   d. 1 silver and 2 bronzes

2. Talented defenseman Garth Butcher was drafted 10th overall by the Canucks but did not score much for them in the NHL. In the 1988-89 season, for example, his first goal did not come until the first round of the playoffs.

   a. True
   b. False

3. Which European defenseman won the Babe Pratt Trophy (given to the Canucks' best defender) four times during the 1990s?

a. Mattias Ohlund

b. Sami Salo

c. Jyrki Lumme

d. Lars Lindgren

4. 4. What did popular magazine *The Hockey News* call Vancouver defenseman Dennis Kearns?

a. "the Denis Potvin of the West"

b. "the next great Canadian defenseman of the 1970s"

c. "a wizard with the puck on his stick and a solid fellow to have in a scrum"

d. "Bobby Orr's little brother, separated at birth"

5. Defenseman Chris Tanev went undrafted by the entire NHL and was plucked as a free agent by Vancouver out of which unlikely college?

a. University of Phoenix Online

b. Texas El Paso State

c. Rochester Institute of Technology

d. College of American Samoa

6. Which defender has played more minutes on the Canucks' blue line than anyone else?

a. Ed Jovanovski

b. Alexander Edler

c. Kevin Bieksa

d. Mattias Ohlund

7. Although other teams offered longer contracts and more money, free agent defenseman Dan Hamhuis signed with

Vancouver in 2010 because he had grown up in British Columbia as a fan of the team.

a. True
b. False

8. In which country did longtime Canuck Mattias Ohlund play his first NHL game?

a. Canada
b. United States of America
c. Sweden
d. Japan

9. The Vancouver Canucks drafted which father and son duo 24 years apart, after the father had spent a nice career on the Vancouver blue line?

a. Garth Butcher and his son Matt
b. Bob Dailey and his son Eric
c. Murray Baron and his son Mark
d. Dam Hamhuis and his son Bradley

10. Which popular Canucks defender, known for his friendly personality and large moustache, loved Vancouver enough to re-sign with the team as a free agent after having been traded to the Minnesota North Stars?

a. Dennis Kearns
b. Harold Snepsts
c. Kevin McCarthy
d. Troy Stecher

11. Defenseman Dennis Kearns played his entire 10-year NHL career with the Vancouver Canucks after they claimed him from which team in the 1971 Intra-League Draft?

    a. New York Rangers

    b. Montreal Canadiens

    c. Chicago Blackhawks

    d. Toronto Maple Leafs

12. Vancouver blueliner Dave Babych was the first NHLer to wear jersey number 44 on a permanent basis.

    a. True

    b. False

13. Canucks mainstay Harold Snepsts played over 750 NHL games with the club. Where does he rank in games played all-time for Vancouver?

    a. 2nd

    b. 4th

    c. 6th

    d. 8th

14. Which team signed a 5-year, $10 million offer sheet with Canucks defenseman Mattias Ohlund in 1997, forcing Vancouver to match the offer to keep him?

    a. Detroit Red Wings

    b. Toronto Maple Leafs

    c. Tampa Bay Lightning

    d. New Jersey Devils

15. What happened to tough guy Kevin Bieksa 10 seconds into his very first NHL shift against the Los Angeles Kings?

    a. He was whistled for a roughing penalty and sent to the penalty box.
    b. He scored his first NHL goal when a shot deflected off of his butt.
    c. He started a fight with noted Kings enforcer Sean Avery.
    d. He threw a body check on Jeremy Roenick that was so hard, it broke a pane of glass in the boards.

16. Vancouver defenseman Brent Sopel once missed a playoff game after injuring his back while picking up a cracker that his daughter had dropped.

    a. True
    b. False

17. Which of the following facts about Canucks defender Dana Murzyn's post-playing career is NOT true?

    a. For a time, he worked as a butcher.
    b. He invested some of his money in a liquor store business.
    c. He joined a local jazz band and played saxophone at gigs.
    d. He made spec homes in the interior regions of British Columbia.

18. Which current Canucks defenseman has the longest tenure in Vancouver?

a. Tyler Myers

b. Alexander Edler

c. Quinn Hughes

d. Oscar Fantenberg

19. In 2006, the Canucks did not offer star defenseman Ed Jovanovski a contract after he became an unrestricted free agent. Why not?

a. He was already on record as wanting to play in a location that had warmer weather and was more tax-friendly.

b. The team considered him to be on the downswing of his career, even though he wound up playing eight more NHL seasons.

c. It was rumored that Jovanovski had conducted an affair with teammate Markus Naslund's wife.

d. The contracts of Daniel Sedin, Henrik Sedin, and Roberto Luongo ate up their available salary cap space.

20. Undrafted defender Chris Tanev was found by the Vancouver Canucks thanks to a connection with his childhood roller hockey coach.

a. True

b. False

QUIZ ANSWERS

1. D – 1 silver and 2 bronzes

2. A – True

3. C – Jyrki Lumme

4. A – "the Denis Potvin of the West"

5. C – Rochester Institute of Technology

6. B – Alexander Edler

7. A – True

8. D – Japan

9. A – Garth Butcher and his son Matt

10. B – Harold Snepsts

11. C – Chicago Blackhawks

12. A – True

13. D – 8th

14. B – Toronto Maple Leafs

15. A – He was whistled for a roughing penalty and sent to the penalty box.

16. A – True

17. C – He joined a local jazz band and played saxophone at gigs.

18. B – Alexander Edler

19. D – The contracts of Daniel Sedin, Henrik Sedin, and Roberto Luongo ate up their available salary cap space.

20. A – True

DID YOU KNOW?

1. Defenseman Doug Lidster played nearly a decade for the Canucks, from 1984-93. His timing was incredible though, as, in 1993, Vancouver traded him to the New York Rangers. He became a Stanley Cup champion that very year, winning with the Rangers in seven games over his former Canucks teammates.

2. Canucks defender Sami Salo was very good on the ice...but also very injury prone. During his career, Salo suffered over 40 injuries, and missed games due to ailments including: recurring shoulder, foot, and knee problems; flu, a snakebite, broken teeth, concussions, a broken finger, back spasms, nerve damage, a groin injury, a fractured wrist, a broken nose, a broken rib, torn pelvis muscles, and a nearly ruptured testicle.

3. One of the more religious Canucks was defenseman Dan Hamhuis. Hamhuis was raised in a Christian household and was very open about his faith around teammates. After joining the Canucks, he organized an optional chapel service for players to attend.

4. Just as Swedes Daniel and Henrik Sedin are littered atop the Canucks leaderboards for forwards, Swedes Alexander Edler and Mattias Ohlund do the same for defensemen. Edler and Ohlund are first and second in goals, assists, points, and games played in franchise history.

5. Canucks defenseman Rick Lanz remained in British Columbia after his retirement and coached several minor league teams. Lanz helped develop several future NHL players, including Milan Lucic, Scott Gomez, Kyle Turris, Keith Seabrook, and Ben Walter.

6. Kevin Bieksa was known as a tough, mean defenseman for the Canucks, but he showed off his lighter side by roasting Daniel and Henrik Sedin in a speech during their jersey retirement ceremony at Rogers Arena. He drew many laughs by noting that Daniel had "a legitimate candy addiction. He eats half of his body weight in sour keys and Swedish berries every Saturday."

7. Only two Canucks defenseman have ever recorded a hat trick with the team. Dave Babych did it once in the regular season in a 1991 game against the Calgary Flames, and Doug Halward also torched the Flames for 3 goals in a playoff game in 1984.

8. One Canucks defender was popular enough to have a song written about him. A band from Hamilton, Ontario, called the Dik Van Dykes created a song called "Harold Snepsts." The band was not famous but did open for The Ramones for a few shows.

9. When the Canucks decided to rebuild during the 1983-84 season, there was a purge in which three of their top defenders were dealt away in quick succession. Kevin McCarthy was sent to Pittsburgh, while Harold Snepsts and Lars Lindgren were both dealt to the Minnesota North Stars.

10. Canucks defender Bret Hedican met fellow American Kristi Yamaguchi, a famous figure skater, while both were part of the 1992 United States Olympic team. The two later married and have two daughters together.

CHAPTER 10:

CENTERS OF ATTENTION

QUIZ TIME!

1. How tall was Canucks center Cliff Ronning, who was repeatedly told he was too small to make it in the NHL before he proved doubters wrong with a 1,137 game career?

   a. 5'2"

   b. 5'4"

   c. 5'6"

   d. 5'8"

2. Center Henrik Sedin and his brother Daniel were the first set of twins to ever play in the NHL.

   a. True

   b. False

3. How did the Canucks fare during superstar Mark Messier's three seasons with the team?

a. Lost in the second round, missed the playoffs, lost in the first round

b. Lost in the Stanley Cup Finals, lost in the first round twice

c. Missed the playoffs twice, lost in the second round

d. Missed the playoffs three times

4. Which of the following players was NOT among the first three Europeans to ever take the ice for the Vancouver Canucks during the 1978 season?

a. Ivan Boldirev

b. Lars Zetterstrom

c. Lars Lindgren

d. Thomas Gradin

5. Popular Canucks center Ivan Boldirev was born in which country before moving to Canada at a young age?

a. Italy

b. Poland

c. Yugoslavia

d. Hungary

6. Which two activities did longtime Canucks center Chris Oddleifson pursue after his playing days with the team came to an end?

a. Selling real estate and playing hockey with the Canucks' old-timer team

b. Scouting minor league players and appearing at professional speaking engagements

c. Coaching his son's high school hockey team and running a barber shop

d. Driving long-haul truck shipments and pioneering the X Games

7. Canucks pivot Bobby Lalonde was the shortest player in the NHL while he was playing, at only 5'5" tall.

a. True
b. False

8. Which Canucks center worked with 2K Sports to help them capture realistic player motion for their NHL 2K10 video game, before appearing on the cover of the NHL 2K11 game?

a. Henrik Sedin
b. Brendan Morrison
c. Mats Sundin
d. Ryan Kesler

9. Four Canucks centers have recorded back-to-back 50 assist seasons for the club. Which of these four players also played his minor hockey in Nanaimo and Victoria, British Columbia?

a. Thomas Gradin
b. Andre Boudrias
c. Barry Pederson
d. Henrik Sedin

10. Against which team did Canucks center Matt Cooke score, with just 5 seconds remaining, in Game 7 of the team's 2004 playoff series?

a. Calgary Flames

b. Edmonton Oilers

c. San Jose Sharks

d. Los Angeles Kings

11. Which current NHL player is a cousin of Vancouver center Bo Horvat?

   a. Calgary Flames center Sean Monahan

   b. Buffalo Sabres winger Jeff Skinner

   c. St. Louis Blues center Ryan O'Reilly

   d. Philadelphia Flyers forward Travis Konecny

12. Vancouver center Richard Lemieux was not a famous name in the NHL but became much more famous when his son Mario entered the league with the Pittsburgh Penguins.

   a. True

   b. False

13. Multiple Vancouver centers held the franchise record for most consecutive games played. Of the following options, who passed who to take over the record?

   a. Ryan Kesler passed Petr Nedved

   b. Henrik Sedin passed Brendan Morrison

   c. Henrik Sedin passed Barry Pederson

   d. Brendan Morrison passed Petr Nedved

14. Young Canucks captain Bo Horvat's first name is actually the short form of which given name?

a. Robert

b. Bowie

c. Beaufort

d. Bones

15. Which of the following facts about Swedish Canucks center Elias Pettersson is NOT true?

    a. He was the second Canuck to take home the Calder Trophy as rookie of the year.

    b. He signed the highest contract extension ever recorded by a Canucks center.

    c. He owns the Canucks franchise record for points scored by a rookie.

    d. He got extra ice time as a child because his father drove the Zamboni at the local rink.

16. Young center Petr Nedved earned a lot of criticism from fans after asking for a stick from his idol Wayne Gretzky after the Canucks were eliminated by Gretzky's Kings in a playoff series.

    a. True

    b. False

17. What unusual record did Canucks center Artem Chubarov set during the 1999-2002 seasons?

    a. First NHL player to play three consecutive seasons without recording a single point

    b. First NHL player to win over 90% of his faceoffs taken

    c. First NHL player to play all five offensive positions in multiple seasons

d. First NHL player to start his career with four consecutive game-winning goals

18. Which team attempted to steal center Ryan Kesler from the Vancouver Canucks in 2006 by signing him to the first NHL offer sheet proposed since 1999?

    a. Anaheim Ducks
    b. Edmonton Oilers
    c. Philadelphia Flyers
    d. New York Rangers

19. Russian center Igor Larionov drank a glass of red wine before every game, and in retirement became a winemaker himself. Which of the following is NOT a label that he produced?

    a. Slapshot
    b. Five-Hole
    c. Hattrick
    d. Triple Overtime

20. Center Orland Kurtenbach recorded the first hat trick in Vancouver history, which was also the only hat trick of his NHL career.

    a. True
    b. False

QUIZ ANSWERS

1. D – 5'8"

2. B – False

3. D – Missed the playoffs three times

4. A – Ivan Boldirev

5. C – Yugoslavia

6. A – Selling real estate and playing hockey with the Canucks' old-timer team

7. A – True

8. D – Ryan Kesler

9. C – Barry Pederson

10. A – Calgary Flames

11. D – Philadelphia Flyers forward Travis Konecny

12. B – False

13. B – Henrik Sedin passed Brendan Morrison

14. B – Bowie

15. B – He signed the highest contract extension ever recorded by a Canucks center.

16. A – True

17. D – First NHL player to start his career with four consecutive game-winning goals

18. C – Philadelphia Flyers

19. B – Five-Hole

20. A – True

DID YOU KNOW?

1. Top Canucks center Petr Nedved would not have been able to play for the team had he not defected to Canada during an international midget tournament in Calgary in 1989. Nedved left Czechoslovakia behind with just $20 to his name and did not even tell his parents about his decision beforehand.

2. Vancouver center Brendan Morrison had quite the swing in luck in the 2007-08 NHL season. Morrison had played 542 consecutive games (the 11th longest streak in league history) before he finally sat out due to a wrist injury that needed surgery. When he returned, he only lasted until the next month before he was knocked out again, this time with a knee injury.

3. The NHL record for most points scored in a playoff game was held by Wayne Gretzky, with seven; until 1988, when Canucks center Patrik Sundstrom finished with eight in a 10-4 Vancouver victory over the Washington Capitals. Sundstrom still owns a piece of the record, though he has since been tied by Mario Lemieux.

4. Very few players can claim as many NHL family members as Canucks center Brandon Sutter. His father Brent, five uncles (Brian, Darryl, Duane, Ron, and Rich), and cousins Brett and Brody have all suited up for NHL teams.

5. Slick center Henrik Sedin led the NHL in assists for three

straight years during his Canucks tenure, and became only the fifth NHL player in history to accomplish that feat. His esteemed company includes Stan Mikita, Bobby Orr, Wayne Gretzky, and Joe Thornton.

6. Finnish center Markus Granlund is one of the rare players who has suited up for all three western Canadian teams. Granlund was drafted by the Calgary Flames, traded to the Vancouver Canucks, and later signed with the Edmonton Oilers as a free agent.

7. Swedish center Thomas Gradin was a gift that kept on giving to the Canucks. Not only did he establish himself as their all-time leading scorer (He has since been passed.), but after retirement, he returned to Sweden and scouted for Vancouver, helping them find franchise mainstays Daniel Sedin, Henrik Sedin, Alexander Edler, and Mattias Ohlund.

8. Outspoken Russian, Igor Larionov, was initially prohibited from travelling internationally with the Russian squad because of fear that he would defect to North America. In 1989-90, he was finally allowed to leave to play in Vancouver because the Soviet Union's governing body for sports needed the money they would receive from the paychecks of Larionov and other players permitted to make the move to the NHL.

9. The first NHL player to pick a fight with superstar Mario Lemieux was Canucks center Gary Lupul in 1984. Unfortunately, the 5'9" Lupul did not fare well against

Lemieux, and Vancouver goalie John Garrett had to join the fight to save Lupul. Garrett was tossed from the game as the third man in.

10. Steve Tambellini would go on to hold numerous positions with the Canucks after his retirement, ranging from director of public and media relations to senior vice president of hockey operations, to assistant general manager.

CHAPTER 11:

THE WINGERS TAKE FLIGHT

QUIZ TIME!

1. Which Canucks winger became the first-ever NHL player from Denmark to play in the postseason, after admitting he'd never even dreamed of playing in the NHL, because no one from his country ever had while he was growing up?

   a. Jere Gillis

   b. Loui Eriksson

   c. Jannik Hansen

   d. Jarkko Ruutu

2. Many Canadian newspapers once reported that winger Pavel Bure threatened to sit out of key playoff games if he was not given a contract extension to his liking.

   a. True

   b. False

3. Which Canucks winger scored the game-winning goal in overtime of Game 5 of the Western Conference Finals in

1994, sending the team on their second-ever trip to the Stanley Cup Finals?

a. Pavel Bure

b. Geoff Courtnall

c. Jake Virtanen

d. Greg Adams

4. What caused Canucks winger Todd Bertuzzi to be suspended indefinitely in 2003-04, missing the end of the regular season and the playoffs?

a. He yelled a racial slur at an opposing player that was picked up by a broadcast microphone.

b. He punched Colorado Avalanche Steve Moore from behind and drove Moore's head into the ice.

c. He threw a knee-on-knee hit on Detroit Red Wing Sergei Fedorov.

d. He gambled on a hockey game during a trip to Las Vegas in the middle of the season.

5. Canucks winger Dennis Ververgaert once held the record (since broken) for the fastest two goals scored in an NHL All-Star Game. How long did it take him to score those goals?

a. 8 seconds

b. 27 seconds

c. 10 seconds

d. 22 seconds

6. How long after arriving in North America did it take Canucks winger Pavel Bure to marry American model Jayme Bohn?

   a. 5 days
   b. 5 weeks
   c. 5 months
   d. 5 years

7. Multiple times in their careers, Canucks left winger Daniel Sedin and his twin brother Henrik took identical contracts when re-signing with Vancouver.

   a. True
   b. False

8. Which winger was the first to play in 1,000 career games with the Canucks franchise?

   a. Trevor Linden
   b. Stan Smyl
   c. Daniel Sedin
   d. Don Lever

9. The right wing spot on Daniel and Henrik Sedin's line was filled mostly by which player during their first few years in the league?

   a. Zack Kassian
   b. Trent Klatt
   c. Sven Baertschi
   d. Jarkko Ruutu

10. Why was Vancouver winger Pavel Bure the only Calder Trophy winning player ever to be left off of the NHL's All-Rookie Team?

   a. He requested not to be on the team because more NHL notoriety would make things harder for his younger brother Valeri, who was still playing back in Russia.
   b. There was still an anti-Russian bias in the league at the time, so the league named a Canadian instead.
   c. He got votes at both the left-wing and right-wing positions, and therefore not enough to win either of the positions.
   d. The general managers who voted on the award were protesting that Bure should not have been eligible to have been drafted the previous year.

11. Which of the following occupations did former Canuck Rick Blight NOT pursue after his NHL career came to an end?

   a. Stockbroker
   b. Farm manager
   c. Marketing consultant
   d. Race car driver

12. The talented Tony Tanti continued his alliterative naming by titling his two tots Taylor and Tessa.

   a. True
   b. False

13. What caused Vancouver right winger Trevor Linden to learn to play center later in his career?

   a. Linden felt that he could ask for a larger contract if he took on more on-ice responsibilities.

   b. After a teammate's lost faceoff in the NHL playoffs led to a goal that eliminated the Canucks, Linden wanted to be the one to take the draw next time.

   c. Coach Pat Quinn requested it after the team lost two centers one offseason.

   d. Injuries to two centers while the team was on a road trip forced the move out of necessity.

14. Which Canucks winger is a member of the Canadian and International Ball Hockey Hall of Fame, and was once named International Ball Hockey Player of the Year?

   a. Greg Adams
   b. Alexandre Burrows
   c. Brock Boeser
   d. Martin Gelinas

15. Popular Canucks winger Gino Odjick starred in a Canadian short film made in 2014. What was the title of this film?

   a. Life and Times of the Algonquin Enforcer
   b. Puck Patrol: Defending Your Hometown
   c. When Coyote Met River Crosser
   d. Ronny Nomad and the Legendary Napkins of Wood

16. Right winger Trevor Linden was not just athletic, but also intelligent and was offered a scholarship to Princeton University.

    a. True
    b. False

17. Which winger broke the 40-goal mark three times with Vancouver and was seen as the team's first "true sniper"?

    a. Pavel Bure
    b. Tony Tanti
    c. Markus Naslund
    d. Alexander Mogilny

18. One Vancouver winger later became a mixed martial arts fighter and won his first fight via technical knockout in just 21 seconds. Which player was this?

    a. Gino Odjick
    b. Alexandre Burrows
    c. Donald Brashear
    d. Todd Bertuzzi

19. Winger Pavel Bure's father and grandfather were excellent athletes who competed in which sports at the Olympic and National levels?

    a. Swimming and water polo
    b. Hockey and baseball
    c. Speed skating and decathlon
    d. Bobsled and luge

20. Canucks winger Markus Naslund was born within 10 days of fellow Swedish star Peter Forsberg, and in addition to playing hockey together, the two worked jobs at the same electrical company together growing up.

    a. True
    b. False

QUIZ ANSWERS

1. C – Jannik Hansen

2. A – True

3. D – Greg Adams

4. B – He punched Colorado Avalanche Steve Moore from behind and drove Moore's head into the ice.

5. C – 10 seconds

6. A – 5 days

7. A – True

8. A – Trevor Linden

9. B – Trent Klatt

10. C – He got votes at both the left-wing and right-wing positions, and therefore not enough to win either of the positions.

11. D – Race car driver

12. A – True

13. C – Coach Pat Quinn requested it after the team lost two centers one offseason.

14. B – Alexandre Burrows

15. D – *Ronny Nomad and the Legendary Napkins of Wood*

16. A – True

17. B – Tony Tanti

18. C – Donald Brashear

19. A – Swimming and water polo

20. A – True

DID YOU KNOW?

1. Canucks right winger Trevor Linden was renowned as a leader, and not only for Vancouver. In 1998, Linden was named president of the National Hockey League Players' Association. It was a post he held for eight years, including during the 2004-05 NHL lockout.

2. The Canucks scouting staff can be credited for stealing star winger Pavel Bure in the 6th round of the 1989 NHL Entry Draft. His talent was obvious, and NHL teams knew that he was eligible to be selected in the top three rounds, but every team was scared that he would not defect from Russia, resulting in a wasted early pick. Vancouver dug deep enough to discover that Bure had played enough additional games to make him eligible for drafting later on in the draft as well, and they capitalized before a few other jealous suitors took the chance.

3. Lifetime Canuck Stan "Steamer" Smyl played his entire career with the team and retired holding many team records (which would eventually be broken). This service to Vancouver earned him the right to be the first Canuck to have his jersey number (12) retired by the franchise.

4. Winger Jim Sandlak was a powerful forward known as "The House." He often struggled to win over Vancouver fans, not because of his play, but because his presence in the organization led to management trading similar player Cam Neely away; a move that would backfire

spectacularly. Sandlak never developed into the force Neely became.

5. Vancouver winger Curt Fraser had dual citizenship and has competed for both the United States of America and Canada in international tournaments. In addition, he has coached in both Belarus and Russia after his retirement.

6. When respected Canucks leader Trevor Linden retired, the City Council of Vancouver officially made the date of his jersey retirement "Trevor Linden Day" in Vancouver. This fell on December 17, 2008.

7. Winger Petri "The Streak" Skriko was the first-ever Finnish player to play for Vancouver. He was also the first Vancouver Canuck to win NHL Player of the Month honors. This occurred in November of 1986 after the high-scoring Skriko posted three hat tricks over just eight days.

8. Brash Canucks winger Todd Bertuzzi once tried to get under the skin of Minnesota fans and players during a 2003 playoff series. He told fans they wouldn't need their Game 6 tickets since the Wild would be eliminated by then and told Wild players on the bench to "get [their] golf clubs." The trash talk would backfire when the Wild came back to eliminate the Canucks in seven games.

9. The Sedin twins made history as the first brothers in the NHL to win back-to-back scoring titles in 2009-10 and 2010-11. Max and Doug Bentley had both won with the Chicago Blackhawks in the 1940s, but never in consecutive seasons.

10. Noted Canucks enforcer Donald Brashear developed much of his toughness as a defense mechanism during a difficult childhood. His father and stepfather were both abusive, to the point where Brashear's mother eventually sent him into foster care.

CHAPTER 12:

COACHES, GMS, & OWNERS

QUIZ TIME!

1. Who served as the Canucks' first general manager?

    a. Scotty Bowman

    b. Jake Milford

    c. Phil Maloney

    d. Bud Poile

2. Despite existing since just 1970, the Vancouver Canucks have hired and fired more head coaches than fellow Canadian teams Montreal and Toronto.

    a. True

    b. False

3. The Canucks' first head coach, Hal Laycoe, lasted for how long in that position with the franchise?

    a. 36 games

    b. 1 season

    c. 2 seasons

    d. 10 seasons

4. Which two Vancouver general managers once skated as players on the team before getting the chance to guide it from the front office?

   a. Jim Benning and Pat Quinn
   b. Hal Laycoe and Brian Burke
   c. Phil Maloney and Dave Nonis
   d. Jake Milford and Mike Gillis

5. Who has owned the Vancouver Canucks for the longest amount of time?

   a. Tom Scallen
   b. Frank Griffiths
   c. Arthur Griffiths
   d. Francesco Aquilini

6. Who is the Vancouver leader in all-time coaching wins with the franchise?

   a. Mike Keenan
   b. Orland Kurtenbach
   c. Alain Vigneault
   d. Pat Quinn

7. Microsoft founder Bill Gates once put in a bid to own the Vancouver Canucks, but the NHL turned down his proposal, fearing he would move the team out of Canada.

   a. True
   b. False

8. Where did former Canucks general manager Brian Burke earn his post-secondary degree?

a. Simon Fraser University

b. Harvard Law School

c. Massachusetts Institute of Technology

d. Brock University

9. Which coach led the Canucks to their second Stanley Cup Finals appearance before giving up the position to become president and general manager?

a. Pat Quinn

b. Roger Neilson

c. Rick Ley

d. Mike Keenan

10. How many of the Canucks' 19 head coaches have spent their entire NHL coaching career with Vancouver?

a. 0

b. 1

c. 4

d. 8

11. Canucks owner Tom Scallen did NOT have an ownership stake in which of the following (either personally or through his company)?

a. Ice Capades

b. Harlem Globetrotters

c. Chanhassen Dinner Theatres

d. Carnival Cruise Lines

12. Mike Keenan and Roger Neilson have coached more NHL teams (including the Canucks) than any other coaches the organization has had, leading eight teams each.

a. True

b. False

13. One-time Vancouver owner John McCaw Jr. has also owned two other professional sports franchises. Which ones did he own?

    a. Vancouver Grizzlies and Force India Racing
    b. Seattle Supersonics and Seattle Seahawks
    c. Inter Milan and Portland Trailblazers
    d. Buffalo Bills and Buffalo Bandits

14. Which Canucks general manager has led the franchise to the most playoff appearances?

    a. Harry Neale
    b. Mike Gillis
    c. Pat Quinn
    d. Dave Nonis

15. Canucks head coach Willie Desjardin was behind the bench for the team from 2014-2017 in his first NHL coaching job. How many years had he been coaching before getting that opportunity?

    a. 2 years
    b. 9 years
    c. 14 years
    d. 30 years

16. Vancouver is the only NHL franchise to have a player rise to ownership of the team.

    a. True
    b. False

17. How did Arthur Griffiths become the majority owner of the Vancouver Canucks from 1988-1997?

    a. He purchased the team when the previous owner went bankrupt.
    b. He inherited the team from his father.
    c. As a minority owner, he bought out the shares of two other owners.
    d. He was hired as CEO of the company that owned the team.

18. When coaching the Quebec Nordiques/Colorado Avalanche franchise, Marc Crawford won his division four times in four years. How many times in his seven years in Vancouver did he win the division title?

    a. 0
    b. 1
    c. 4
    d. 7

19. Two Canucks coaches have won the Jack Adams Award as the league's top coach while behind the bench for Vancouver. Which ones took home the hardware?

    a. Mike Keenan and John Tortorella
    b. Pat Quinn and Alain Vigneault
    c. Hal Laycoe and Tom Renney
    d. Roger Neilson and Marc Crawford

20. Canucks owner Francesco Aquilini once proposed trading franchises with San Jose Sharks owner Hasso Plattner as part of a business deal.

a. True

b. False

QUIZ ANSWERS

1. D – Bud Poile

2. B – False

3. C – 2 seasons

4. A – Jim Benning and Pat Quinn

5. D – Francesco Aquilini

6. C – Alain Vigneault

7. B – False

8. B – Harvard Law School

9. A – Pat Quinn

10. C – 4

11. D – Carnival Cruise Lines

12. A – True

13. A – Vancouver Grizzlies and Force India Racing

14. C – Pat Quinn

15. D – 30 years

16. B – False

17. B – He inherited the team from his father.

18. B – 1

19. B – Pat Quinn and Alain Vigneault

20. B – False

DID YOU KNOW?

1. Original Canucks owner Tom Scallen controlled the team from 1970-74. For two years of that tenure, Scallen was imprisoned after being charged with stock fraud. He eventually relinquished control of the team. Scallen was later exonerated and received a full pardon but did not pursue team ownership again.

2. During the 1981-82 season, the Canucks had great success (making it to the Stanley Cup Finals), but still changed coaches from Harry Neale to Roger Neilson during this season. This was because Neale got into an altercation with some fans of the Quebec Nordiques and was suspended before the playoffs began.

3. In 2014, coach John Tortorella elected to start goaltender Eddie Lack in the Heritage Classic. This upset popular goaltender Roberto Luongo, who was traded two days later. It did not go well for Tortorella and his staff either, as they were fired at the end of the season.

4. Four men have served as both coach and general manager of the Vancouver Canucks. Hal Laycoe was the first, and the feat was repeated by Phil Maloney, Harry Neale, and Mike Keenan.

5. Canucks coach Bill McCreary lasted just one season as coach of the Canucks, but his nephew, also named Bill

McCreary, went on to a very lengthy career as an NHL referee who officiated over 1,700 games in the league.

6. In the offseason of 2013, the Canucks and New York Rangers made an interesting decision. Both decided to change coaches. The Canucks hired dismissed Ranger coach John Tortorella, and the Rangers hired former Canucks coach Alain Vigneault, in effect trading coaches between the two teams.

7. Tom Watt began his coaching career as an assistant coach with the Canucks in 1980-81. He left for the head coaching job with the Winnipeg Jets the next year, won the coach of the year award, then returned to the Canucks in 1985-86 as both head coach and assistant general manager.

8. When Roger Neilson took over for Harry Neale during Neale's 10-game suspension, Neilson's Canucks went 9-1 during the stretch, so Neilson was kept on as coach even when Neale was ready to return to the bench.

9. Only once has a Vancouver general manager been awarded the NHL General Manager of the Year Trophy. In 2010-11, Mike Gillis took home the trophy after the Canucks won the President's Trophy with 117 points and advanced to the Stanley Cup Finals.

10. Current Canucks coach Travis Green played for five NHL franchises before turning to coaching after hanging up his skates. Though he never suited up for Vancouver as a player, Green was born in British Columbia and was happy to return home for his first NHL coaching gig.

CHAPTER 13:

THE AWARDS SECTION

QUIZ TIME!

1. Which Canuck has won the most Hart Trophies as league MVP while playing for Vancouver?

   a. Trevor Linden
   b. Pavel Bure
   c. Henrik Sedin
   d. Daniel Sedin

2. The first Canuck to win any major award given out by the NHL was franchise center Trevor Linden in 1996-97.

   a. True
   b. False

3. During which season did the Canucks win their first President's Trophy for leading the NHL in points?

   a. 1982-83
   b. 1993-94
   c. 2010-11
   d. 2011-12

4. Which two Canucks goaltenders shared the franchise's first-ever William M. Jennings Trophy for allowing the fewest goals?

   a. Ryan Miller and Jacob Markstrom
   b. Roberto Luongo and Cory Schneider
   c. Kirk McLean and Bob Essensa
   d. Glen Hanlon and Kay Whitmore

5. Although no Vancouver player has won the Maurice "Rocket" Richard Trophy for most goals in the NHL, one former Canuck won it twice while playing in a different location. Who was it?

   a. Todd Bertuzzi, in Detroit
   b. Cam Neely, in Boston
   c. Pavel Bure, in Florida
   d. Alexander Mogilny, in Buffalo

6. Since 2006, the NHL has given out a leadership award named for which former Canucks player?

   a. Trevor Linden
   b. Roberto Luongo
   c. Cliff Ronning
   d. Mark Messier

7. The Sedin twins, Daniel and Henrik, are the first brothers in the history of the NHL to share the King Clancy Trophy for leadership and community involvement.

   a. True
   b. False

8. Who was the most recent Vancouver player to make the NHL All-Rookie Team?

   a. Bo Horvat
   b. Elias Pettersson
   c. Brock Boeser
   d. Cory Schneider

9. When Canucks bench boss Pat Quinn won the Jack Adams Trophy as coach of the year in 1991-92, it marked the second time he'd won the award. With which franchise did he capture his first?

   a. Vancouver Canucks
   b. Los Angeles Kings
   c. Philadelphia Flyers
   d. Toronto Maple Leafs

10. Which of these iconic Canucks duos have each won an Art Ross Trophy as the league's leading scorer?

   a. Pavel Bure and Alexander Mogilny
   b. Markus Naslund and Todd Bertuzzi
   c. Trevor Linden and Mark Messier
   d. Daniel Sedin and Henrik Sedin

11. The Lady Byng Memorial Trophy for sportsmanship, gentlemanly conduct, and playing ability has been won by how many Canucks in franchise history?

   a. 0
   b. 2
   c. 6
   d. 9

12. Vancouver gives out its own Cyclone Taylor Award, for the most valuable player to the Canucks each year, which has been won more times by Markus Naslund than any other player.

   a. True
   b. False

13. Which of the following Canucks players won the Calder Memorial Trophy as the league's top rookie?

   a. Pavel Bure and Elias Pettersson
   b. Trevor Linden and Pavel Bure
   c. Tony Tanti and Markus Naslund
   d. Don Lever and Bo Horvat

14. Of the Canucks in the Hockey Hall of Fame, Cam Neely is first among them to skate with the Canucks. What year did he begin playing with the team?

   a. 1981
   b. 1983
   c. 1985
   d. 1987

15. Which Canucks player has been selected to the most NHL First All-Star Teams?

   a. Markus Naslund
   b. Daniel Sedin
   c. Roberto Luongo
   d. Pavel Bure

16. The Canucks pass out a Fred J. Hume Award each season,

which is given to the player who racks up the most penalty minutes for the team.

a. True

b. False

17. The James Norris Trophy, given annually to the NHL's best defenseman, has been hoisted by how many Vancouver Canucks throughout the years?

a. 0

b. 1

c. 2

d. 7

18. How many Vancouver Canucks have been elected to the Hall of Fame in the "Builders" category?

a. 1

b. 3

c. 5

d. 7

19. In which years did Vancouver host the NHL's annual All-Star Game?

a. 1972 and 1999

b. 1973 and 2003

c. 1977 and 1998

d. 1985 and 2014

20. Vancouver defenseman Marek Malik won the (now defunct) NHL Plus-Minus Award in 2003-04, after recording a +35 rating for the season.

a. True

b. False

QUIZ ANSWERS

1. C – Henrik Sedin

2. B – False

3. C – 2010-11

4. B – Roberto Luongo and Cory Schneider

5. C – Pavel Bure, in Florida

6. D – Mark Messier

7. A – True

8. B – Elias Pettersson

9. C – Philadelphia Flyers

10. D – Daniel Sedin and Henrik Sedin

11. A – 0

12. A – True

13. A – Pavel Bure and Elias Pettersson

14. B – 1983

15. A – Markus Naslund

16. B – False

17. A – 0

18. C – 5

19. C – 1977 and 1998

20. A – True

DID YOU KNOW?

1. The Bill Masterton Trophy, for perseverance, sportsmanship, and dedication to hockey, has never been won by a Vancouver Canucks player.

2. The only player in the NHL to ever win the Scotiabank/NHL Fan Fav Award was Vancouver goalie Roberto Luongo in 2010. The award was based solely on fan voting, which the popular Luongo excelled in, and was discontinued after only one year in existence.

3. Despite strong goaltending throughout the years, no Vancouver Canuck has ever won the Vezina Trophy as the NHL's best goalie.

4. Six players who skated with Vancouver have been elected to the Hockey Hall of Fame. Three of the six were born in Canada, but Swede Mats Sundin and Russians Igor Larionov and Pavel Bure were also selected for enshrinement. Defenseman Pat Quinn is one of the six, but he was elected to the Hall of Fame in the "Builders" category for his work as head coach, president, and general manager, rather than for his playing career.

5. Only one Vancouver Canuck has ever won the Frank J. Selke Trophy as the best defensive forward in the NHL. Center Ryan Kesler took home the award in 2010-11, showing the team's fantastic depth up the middle (center

Henrik Sedin was the league's most valuable player that year).

6. Vancouver is among 11 NHL teams that have never won a Stanley Cup championship. They are tied with the Buffalo Sabres as the oldest team without a Cup. The Toronto Maple Leafs actually have a longer drought, at 52 years, although the franchise did win championships prior to that.

7. Canucks veteran center Henrik Sedin was blown away when he won the 2010 Hart Memorial Trophy over Sidney Crosby and Alexander Ovechkin. He said the two young superstars were "the faces of the sport...to be standing next to them as the old guy, it's a strange feeling."

8. Two Canucks have taken home the Ted Lindsay Award as the league's most outstanding player. Markus Naslund and Daniel Sedin each won this award (voted on by the NHL Players' Association), despite never claiming the more traditional Hart Trophy.

9. Center Trevor Linden was the first Canuck to win the King Clancy Memorial Trophy for leadership and humanitarian contribution, in 1996-97. He booked a suite at the team's arena and invited underprivileged children to come watch the team play at every home game.

10. Vancouver has created a "Ring of Honour" to celebrate individuals who have made a strong impact with the franchise. Seven people have been inducted, including Pat Quinn, Alex Burrows, Kirk McLean, Orland Kurtenbach, Thomas Gradin, Mattias Ohlund, and Harold Snepsts.

CONCLUSION

There you have it, an amazing collection of Canucks trivia, information, and statistics at your fingertips! Regardless of how you fared on the quizzes, we hope that you found this book entertaining, enlightening, and educational.

Ideally, you knew many of these details, but also learned a good deal more about the history of the Vancouver Canucks, their players, coaches, management, and some of the quirky stories surrounding the team. If you got a little peek into the colorful details that make being a fan so much more enjoyable, then mission accomplished!

The good news is, the trivia doesn't have to stop there! Spread the word. Challenge your fellow Canucks fans to see if they can do any better. Share some of the stories with the next generation to help them become Vancouver supporters too.

If you are a big enough Canucks fan, consider creating your own quiz with some of the details you know that weren't presented here, and then test your friends to see if they can match your knowledge.

The Vancouver Canucks are a storied franchise. They have a

long history with multiple periods of success (and a few that were less than successful). They've had glorious superstars, iconic moments, hilarious tales…but most of all, they have wonderful, passionate fans. Thank you for being one of them.

Made in United States
Troutdale, OR
10/11/2024

23653873R20080